Page-turning Reading practice from CGP!

If you're taking Grade 9-1 AQA GCSE English Language, you'll need to be able to analyse a range of fiction texts... and it's no simple task.

But never fear. This CGP Workbook is packed with brilliant sample texts and indispensable practice questions — all geared towards building the skills you need for a top mark in the Reading section of the AQA Paper 1 exam.

And with crystal-clear answers for every question at the back of the book, you'll have everything you need for a success story on exam day!

Published by CGP

Editors:
Tom Carney
Andy Cashmore
Emma Crighton
Alex Fairer
James Summersgill
Sean Walsh

With thanks to Zoe Fenwick and Paula Barnett for the proofreading.
With thanks to Ana Pungartnik for the copyright research.

ISBN: 978 1 78908 005 6
Printed by Elanders Ltd, Newcastle upon Tyne.

Based on the classic CGP style created by Richard Parsons.

Contents

Exercise A — Mr Norris Changes Trains

Extract from Chapter 2

Written from the perspective of narrator William Bradshaw, Christopher Isherwood's 1935 novel explores the character of Mr Norris, a Communist living in Germany during the rise of Nazism. William and Mr Norris meet on a train and become friends. As the story unfolds, William discovers unusual things about his new friend. In this extract, William has just arrived at Mr Norris's flat.

A moment later Mr Norris himself came into the room, nervously rubbing his manicured hands together.

'My dear boy, this is indeed an honour! Delighted to welcome you under the shadow of my humble roof-tree.'

He didn't look well, I thought. His face wasn't so rosy today, and there were rings under his eyes. He sat down for a moment in an armchair, but rose again immediately, as if he were not in the mood for sitting still. He must have been wearing a different wig, for the joins in this one showed as plain as murder.

'You'd like to see over the flat, I expect?' he asked, nervously touching his temples with the tips of his fingers.

'I should, very much.' I smiled, puzzled because Mr Norris was obviously in a great hurry about something. With fussy haste, he took me by the elbow, steering me towards the door in the opposite wall, from which he himself had just emerged.

'We'll go this way first, yes.'

But hardly had we taken a couple of steps when there was a sudden outburst of voices from the entrance hall.

'You can't. It's impossible,' came the voice of the young man who had ushered me into the flat. And a strange, loud, angry voice answered: 'That's a dirty lie! I tell you he's here!'

Mr Norris stopped as suddenly as if he'd been shot. 'Oh dear!' he whispered, hardly audible. 'Oh dear!' Stricken with indecision and alarm, he stood still in the middle of the room, as though desperately considering which way to turn. His grip on my arm tightened, either for support or merely to implore me to keep quiet.

'Mr Norris will not be back until late this evening.' The young man's voice was no longer apologetic, but firm. 'It's no good your waiting.'

He seemed to have shifted his position and to be just outside, perhaps barring the way into the sitting-room. And, the next moment, the sitting-room door was quietly shut, with a click of a key being turned. We were locked in.

'He's in there!' shouted the strange voice, loud and menacing. There was a scuffling, followed by a heavy thud, as if the young man had been flung violently against the door. The thud roused Mr Norris to action. With a single, surprisingly agile movement, he dragged me after him into the adjoining room. We stood there together in the doorway, ready, at any moment, for further retreat. I could hear him panting heavily at my side.

Meanwhile, the stranger was rattling the sitting-room door as if he meant to burst it open: 'You damned swindler!' he shouted in a terrible voice. 'You wait till I get my hands on you!'

It was all so very extraordinary that I quite forgot to feel frightened, although it might well be supposed that the person on the other side of the door was either raving drunk or insane. I cast a questioning glance at Mr Norris, who whispered reassuringly: 'He'll go away in a minute, I think.' The curious thing was that, although scared, he didn't seem at all surprised by what was taking place. It might have been imagined, from his tone, that he was referring to an unpleasant but frequently recurring natural phenomenon: a violent thunder-storm, for instance. His blue eyes were warily, uneasily alert. His hands rested on the door handle, prepared to slam it shut at an instant's notice.

Q1 In this passage, Isherwood vividly describes the character of Mr Norris.

a) List four things about Mr Norris's appearance that you are told in lines 1-6.

1. ....

2. ....

3. ....

4. ....

b) What is your impression of Mr Norris from these lines? Use examples from the text in your answer.

You might want to use your answers to part a) as evidence for this question.

....

....

....

....

....

....

This extract is tense from the very start thanks to Mr Norris's nervous behaviour. This tension steadily builds as the intruder arrives and then tries to force his way into Mr Norris's flat.

Q2 Isherwood uses language to increase tension when describing Mr Norris and the intruder in lines 13-20. Choose one example for each character and explain how the use of language increases the tension.

Mr Norris: ....

....

....

....

Intruder: ....

....

....

....

Q3 From line 13 to the end of the extract, the focus alternates between the action outside the flat, and Mr Norris and William inside the flat. How does this help to create tension?

Q4 Isherwood uses descriptions of sound in lines 23-32.

Choose two sounds from these lines. What effect do each of these sounds have?

1.

2.

Q5 "The narrative viewpoint is what keeps the reader interested in the text." How far do you agree with this?

Extension Activity

WRITING TASK

Isherwood keeps the reader in the dark about what's going on. Have a go at writing about a time when someone was secretive towards you — it could be real or made-up. How did they behave? How did it make you feel? You could then write about discovering what their secret was.

Exercise B — The Thirteenth Tale

Extract from Chapter 1

This extract from Diane Setterfield's 2006 novel is part of a letter from Vida Winter, an ageing author, to Margaret Lea, an amateur biographer. For years, Winter has told lies about herself to inquisitive journalists, but now she has decided to ask Lea to publish the truth about her life.

I've nothing against people who love truth. Apart from the fact that they make dull companions. Just so long as they don't start on about storytelling and honesty, the way some of them do. Naturally that annoys me. Provided they leave me alone, I won't hurt them.

My gripe is not with lovers of truth but with truth herself. What succour*, what consolation is there in truth, compared to a story? What good is truth, at midnight, in the dark, when the wind is roaring like a bear in the chimney? When the lightning strikes shadows on the bedroom wall and the rain taps at the window with its long fingernails? No. When fear and cold make a statue of you in your bed, don't expect hard-boned and fleshless truth to come running to your aid. What you need are the plump comforts of a story. The soothing, rocking safety of a lie.

Some writers don't like interviews, of course. They get cross about it. 'Same old questions,' they complain. Well, what do they expect? Reporters are hacks. We writers are the real thing. Just because they always ask the same questions, it doesn't mean we have to give them the same old answers, does it? I mean, making things up, it's what we do for a living. So I give dozens of interviews a year. Hundreds over the course of a lifetime. For I have never believed that genius needs to be locked away out of sight to thrive. My genius is not so frail a thing that it cowers from the dirty fingers of the newspaper men.

In the early years they used to try and catch me out. They would do research, come along with a little piece of truth concealed in their pocket, draw it out at an opportune moment and hope to startle me into revealing more. I had to be careful. Inch them in the direction I wanted them to take, use my bait to draw them gently, imperceptibly*, towards a prettier story than the one they had their eye on. A delicate operation. Their eyes would start to shine, and their grasp on the little chip of truth would loosen, until it dropped from their hand and fell, disregarded, by the wayside. It never failed. A good story is always more dazzling than a broken piece of truth.

Afterwards, once I became famous, the Vida Winter interview became a sort of rite of passage for journalists. They knew roughly what to expect, would have been disappointed to leave without the story. A quick run through the normal questions (Where do you get your inspiration? Are your characters based on real people? How much of your main character is you?) and the shorter my answers the better they liked it (Inside my head. No. None.) Then, the bit they were waiting for, the thing they had really come for. A dreamy, expectant look stole across their faces. They were like children at bedtime. And you, Miss Winter, they said. Tell me about yourself.

And I told. Simple little stories really, not much to them. Just a few strands, woven together in a pretty pattern, a memorable motif here, a couple of sequins there. Mere scraps from the bottom of my rag-bag. Hundreds more where they came from. Offcuts from novels and stories, plots that never got finished, stillborn characters, picturesque locations I never found a use for. Odds and ends that fell out in the editing. Then it's just a matter of neatening the edges, stitching in the ends, and it's done. Another brand new biography.

Glossary:
succour — support or help
imperceptibly — in a slight and unnoticeable way

Q1 Winter discusses truth and lies in the first two paragraphs of this extract.

a) Based on the first two paragraphs, describe Winter's attitude to truth.

....

....

....

b) Read lines 7-9 again. How is language used to describe truth? What effect does this have?

....

....

....

c) How is language used to describe lies in lines 7-9? What effect does this have?

....

....

....

Q2 In the third, fourth and fifth paragraphs, Winter describes her experiences with reporters.

a) What do the third and fourth paragraphs tell you about Winter's attitude towards reporters? Use examples from the text in your answer.

....

....

....

....

....

b) How does the writer use structure for effect in the third, fourth and fifth paragraphs?

....

....

....

....

....

Q3 "My genius is not so frail a thing that it cowers from the dirty fingers of the newspaper men." (line 15). How is language used here to suggest that Winter is a confident character?

....

....

....

....

....

....

Q4 Vida Winter frequently lies about her life. How does the writer use language in this extract to suggest that Winter is an effective liar?

You might want to think about:

- which words and phrases the writer has chosen
- how the writer has used imagery.

....

....

....

....

....

....

....

....

....

....

....

....

....

Think about the text's narrative voice...

Writers make deliberate choices when deciding which narrative viewpoint to use. A first-person narrator can establish a strong connection with the reader, a second-person narrator often tries to make the reader feel what the character is feeling, and a third-person narrator can create a more detached viewpoint. It's important to think about why the writer has chosen a certain narrative viewpoint and the effect it has.

Exercise C — The Adventure of the Priory School

Adapted extract from the end of the short story

Arthur Conan Doyle's short story from 1904 features the fictional private detective Sherlock Holmes. In this extract, a Duke tells Holmes about how James Wilder, his illegitimate son, kidnapped his legitimate heir, Arthur. In the process of kidnapping Arthur, a German teacher called Heidegger was killed by James's accomplice, Hayes. In this extract, the Duke has just revealed that James is his son.

It was Holmes's turn to look astonished.

"I confess that this is entirely new to me, your Grace. I must beg you to be more explicit."

"I will conceal nothing from you. I agree with you that complete frankness, however painful it may be to me, is the best policy in this desperate situation. When I was a very young man, Mr. Holmes, I loved with such a love as comes only once in a lifetime. I offered the lady marriage, but she refused it on the grounds that such a match might mar my career. Had she lived, I would certainly never have married anyone else. She died, and left this one child, whom for her sake I have cherished and cared for. I could not acknowledge the paternity to the world, but I gave him the best of educations, and since he came to manhood I have kept him near my person. He surmised* my secret, and has presumed ever since upon the claim which he has upon me, and upon his power of provoking a scandal which would be abhorrent to me. Above all, he hated my young legitimate heir from the first with a persistent hatred. You may well ask me why, under these circumstances, I still kept James under my roof. I answer that it was because I could see his mother's face in his, and that for her dear sake there was no end to my long-suffering. I *could* not send him away. But I feared so much lest he should do Arthur a mischief, that I dispatched him for safety to Dr. Huxtable's school.

"You remember that I wrote to Arthur. Well, James opened the letter and inserted a note asking Arthur to meet him in a little wood called the Ragged Shaw, which is near to the school. He used the Duchess's name, and in that way got the boy to come. That evening James bicycled over — I am telling you what he has himself confessed to me — and he told Arthur, whom he met in the wood, that his mother longed to see him, that she was awaiting him on the moor, and that if he would come back into the wood at midnight he would find a man with a horse, who would take him to her. Poor Arthur fell into the trap. It appears — though this James only heard yesterday — that they were pursued, that Hayes struck the pursuer with his stick, and that the man died of his injuries.

"Well, Mr. Holmes, that was the state of affairs when I first saw you two days ago. I had no more idea of the truth than you. You will ask me what was James's motive in doing such a deed. I answer that there was a great deal which was unreasoning and fanatical in the hatred which he bore my heir. In his view he should himself have been heir of all my estates, and he deeply resented those social laws which made it impossible. He intended to make a bargain with me — to restore Arthur if I would break the entail, and so make it possible for the estate to be left to him by will.

"What brought all his wicked scheme to wreck was your discovery of this man Heidegger's dead body. James was seized with horror at the news. He was so overwhelmed with grief and agitation that my suspicions, which had never been entirely absent, rose instantly to a certainty, and I taxed him with the deed. He made a complete voluntary confession.

Then he implored me to keep his secret for three days longer, so as to give his wretched accomplice a chance of saving his guilty life. I yielded — as I have always yielded — to his prayers. I found Arthur safe and well, but horrified beyond expression by the dreadful deed he had witnessed. In deference* to my promise, and much against my will, I consented to leave him there for three days, since it was evident that it was impossible to inform the police where he was without telling them also who was the murderer, and I could not see how that murderer could be punished without ruin to my unfortunate James. You asked for frankness, Mr. Holmes,and I have taken you at your word, for I have now told you everything without an attempt at circumlocution* or concealment. Do you in turn be as frank with me."

Glossary:
surmised — guessed
deference — respect
circumlocution — the use of more words than are necessary

Q1 Sherlock Holmes's only dialogue in the extract is in line 2. What does Holmes's language in this line suggest about his character? Use examples in your answer.

....

....

....

....

....

In the early 20th century, when this short story is set, having a child outside of marriage was considered shameful by society. Inheritance went to legitimate heirs unless the person who was passing on the inheritance was willing to "break the entail" (lines 29-30), which meant cutting off the inheritance to an heir.

Q2 Read the account the Duke gives to Holmes in lines 3-15.
Summarise what we learn about the story so far in this paragraph.

....

....

....

....

....

....

....

....

Q3 According to this extract, James's plot didn't go to plan.
Explain what James's plot was and what would have happened if it had been successful.

Q4 Do you think the reader is supposed to feel any sympathy for James?
Use examples from the extract to explain your answer.

Q5 Early 20th-century texts sometimes use unfamiliar phrasing.

a) What is meant by the phrase "I feared so much lest he should do Arthur a mischief" (line 14)?

b) What is meant by the phrase "brought all his wicked scheme to wreck" (line 31)?

c) What is meant by the phrase "I taxed him with the deed" (line 35)?

Q6 How has the extract been structured to keep you interested?

Q7 The majority of this extract consists of speech from the Duke.

a) What is the effect of having so much speech from the Duke in this extract?

b) What is your overall impression of the Duke?

Extension Activity

Secrets and lies are common themes in mystery and crime genres — in fact, they're almost essential. See if you can think of other examples of secrets and lies (these could be from a book, film or TV show). What effect did they have on the plot? How important are they to the story?

Exercise A — The Miniaturist

Extract from Chapter 1

This extract is from Jessie Burton's debut novel, 'The Miniaturist', which was published in 2014. Set in 17th-century Amsterdam, it tells the story of Petronella (Nella) Oortman, a young Dutch girl who has recently married a rich merchant named Johannes Brandt. In this extract, Nella has just left her rural hometown of Assendelft to live with her new husband in his house in Amsterdam.

Nella cheers silently and stays to face this rare October warmth, to take it while she can. This part of the Herengracht* is known as the Golden Bend, but today the wide stretch is brown and workaday*. Looming above the sludge-coloured canal, the houses are a phenomenon. Admiring their own symmetry on the water, they are stately and beautiful, jewels set within the city's pride. Above their rooftops Nature is doing her best to keep up, and clouds in colours of saffron and apricot echo the spoils of the glorious republic.

Nella turns back to the door, now slightly ajar. Was it like this before? She cannot be sure. She pushes on it, peering into the void as cool air rises from the marble. 'Johannes Brandt?' she calls – loud, a little panicked. Is this a game? she thinks. I'll be standing here come January. Peebo, her parakeet, thrills the tips of his feathers against the cage bars, his faint cheep falling short on the marble. Even the now-quiet canal behind them seems to hold its breath.

Nella is sure of one thing as she looks deeper into the shadows. She's being watched. *Come on, Nella Elizabeth*, she tells herself, stepping over the threshold. Will her new husband embrace her, kiss her or shake her hand like it's just business? He didn't do any of those things at the ceremony, surrounded by her small family and not a single member of his.

To show that country girls have manners too, she bends down and removes her shoes – dainty, leather, of course her best – although what their point has been she can't now say. *Dignity*, her mother said, but dignity is so uncomfortable. She slaps the shoes down, hoping the noise will arouse* somebody, or maybe even scare them off. Her mother calls her over-imaginative, Nella-in-the-Clouds. The inert shoes lie in anti-climax and Nella simply feels a fool.

Outside, two women call to one other. Nella turns, but through the open door she sees only the back of one woman, capless, golden-headed and tall, striding away towards the last of the sun. Nella's own hair has loosened on the journey from Assendelft*, the light breeze letting wisps escape. To tuck them away will make her more nervous than she can bear to seem, so she leaves them tickling her face.

'Are we to have a menagerie?'*

The voice sails sure and swift from the darkness of the hall. Nella's skin contracts, for being right about her suspicions can't banish the goosebumps. She watches as a figure glides from the shadows, a hand outstretched – in protest or in greeting, it is hard to tell. It is a woman, straight and slim and dressed in deepest black, the cap on her head starched and pressed to white perfection. Not a wisp of hair escapes, and she brings with her the vaguest, strangest scent of nutmeg. Her eyes are grey, her mouth is solemn. How long has she been there, watching? Peebo chirrups at the intervention.

Glossary:
Herengracht — a canal in Amsterdam
workaday — ordinary, uninteresting
arouse — cause someone to act
Assendelft — a town in the Netherlands
menagerie — a collection of animals

Q1 In the first paragraph, Nella describes her surroundings.

a) List four things you are told about Nella's surroundings in this extract.

1. ....

2. ....

3. ....

4. ....

b) "The author makes 17th-century Amsterdam sound like a place you would like to live in." Do you agree with this? Give one example from the first paragraph to support your answer.

....

....

....

....

....

Q2 Read line 7. Give one technique that Burton uses in this line and explain its effect.

Technique: ....

Effect: ....

....

....

Q3 At this point in the novel, Nella is 18 years old. Do you think she seems young or childlike in this extract? Explain your answer.

....

....

....

....

....

....

Q4 This extract is written in the present tense. Why do you think Burton chose to do this?

....

....

....

....

There are multiple descriptions of hair in this extract. Nella's hair is described as having "loosened" (line 24), with the breeze "letting wisps escape" (line 25). The woman who has "Not a wisp" (line 35) of hair escaping is Marin, the sister of Nella's new husband.

Q5 What do you think these descriptions of hair might tell you about these characters?

....

....

....

....

....

Q6 The extract has an eerie tone. How has this tone been created?

....

....

....

....

....

....

....

....

....

....

Q7 The author uses sensory language in this extract.

Sensory language includes the senses of sight, sound, smell, taste and touch.

a) Give an example of sensory language from the extract.

....

b) What effect does this use of sensory language have?

....

....

....

....

Q8 "The author makes it easy to understand why Nella is so uncomfortable in this extract." How far do you agree with this statement?

You might want to think about:

- how people and places are presented
- how Nella is presented.

....

....

....

....

....

....

....

....

....

....

....

....

Hunt through the text for language devices...

Always keep an eye out for language devices such as similes, metaphors and personification when you're reading through a text. It's a good idea to underline any that you spot so you can come back to them later and think about what they mean. Make sure you think about why an author has used a particular language device — what effect or impression does it create, and how does it affect the way you read the text?

Exercise B — The Enchanted April

Adapted extract from Chapter 6

'The Enchanted April' by Elizabeth von Arnim was published in 1922. It is about four women in the 1920s who rent an Italian castle together after responding to a newspaper advert. The extract below follows Mrs. Wilkins, one of the four women, who has an unhappy marriage back in England.

When Mrs. Wilkins woke next morning she lay in bed a few minutes before getting up and opening the shutters. What would she see out of her window? A shining world, or a world of rain? But it would be beautiful; whatever it was would be beautiful.

She was in a little bedroom with bare white walls and a stone floor and sparse old furniture. The beds — there were two — were made of iron, enamelled black and painted with bunches of bright flowers. She lay putting off the great moment of going to the window as one puts off opening a precious letter, gloating over it. She had no idea what time it was; she had forgotten to wind up her watch ever since, centuries ago, she last went to bed in Hampstead*. No sounds were to be heard in the house, so she supposed it was very early, yet she felt as if she had slept a long while — so completely rested, so perfectly content. She lay with her arms clasped round her head thinking how happy she was, her lips curved upwards in a delighted smile. In bed by herself: adorable condition. She had not been in a bed without Mellersh once now for five whole years; and the cool roominess of it, the freedom of one's movements, the sense of recklessness, of audacity, in giving the blankets a pull if one wanted to, or twitching the pillows more comfortably! It was like the discovery of an entirely new joy.

Mrs. Wilkins longed to get up and open the shutters, but where she was was really so very delicious. She gave a sigh of contentment, and went on lying there looking round her, taking in everything in her room, her own little room, her very own to arrange just as she pleased for this one blessed month, her room bought with her own savings, the fruit of her careful denials, whose door she could bolt if she wanted to, and nobody had the right to come in. It was such a strange little room, so different from any she had known, and so sweet. It was like a cell. Except for the two beds, it suggested a happy austerity*.

Well, this was delicious, to lie there thinking how happy she was, but outside those shutters it was more delicious still. She jumped up, pulled on her slippers, for there was nothing on the stone floor but one small rug, ran to the window and threw open the shutters.

"Oh!" cried Mrs. Wilkins.

All the radiance of April in Italy lay gathered together at her feet. The sun poured in on her. The sea lay asleep in it, hardly stirring. Across the bay the lovely mountains, exquisitely different in colour, were asleep too in the light; and underneath her window, at the bottom of the flower-starred grass slope from which the wall of the castle rose up, was a great cypress*, cutting through the delicate blues and violets and rose-colours of the mountains and the sea like a great black sword.

She stared. Such beauty; and she there to see it. Such beauty; and she alive to feel it. Her face was bathed in light. Lovely scents came up to the window and caressed her. A tiny breeze gently lifted her hair. Far out in the bay a cluster of almost motionless fishing boats hovered like a flock of white birds on the tranquil sea. How beautiful, how beautiful. Not to have died before this... to have been allowed to see, breathe, feel this... She stared, her lips parted. Happy? Poor, ordinary, everyday word. But what could one say, how could one describe it? It was as though she could hardly stay inside herself, it was as though she were too small to hold so much of joy, it was as though she were washed through with light. And how astonishing to feel this sheer bliss, for here she was, not doing and not going to do a single unselfish thing, not going to do a thing she didn't want to do. According to everybody she had ever come across she ought at least to have twinges. She had not one twinge. Something was wrong somewhere. Wonderful that at home she should have been so good, so terribly good, and merely felt tormented. Twinges of every sort had there been her portion; aches, hurts, discouragements, and she the whole time being steadily unselfish. Now she had taken off all her goodness and left it behind her like a heap in rain-sodden clothes, and she only felt joy. She was naked of goodness, and was rejoicing in being naked. She was stripped, and exulting*. And there, away in the dim mugginess of Hampstead, was Mellersh being angry.

Glossary:
Hampstead — an area of London
austerity — plainness or lack of luxury
cypress — a type of tree
exulting — showing great joy

Q1 Read the description of Mrs. Wilkins's room in the castle in lines 4-5. Does this make the room sound appealing? Explain your answer with references to the text.

....

....

....

....

Q2 What device does the writer use when she writes "ever since, centuries ago, she last went to bed in Hampstead" (lines 7-8)? What does it show about Mrs. Wilkins's feelings?

....

....

....

....

....

Q3 In paragraph three, the writer describes Mrs. Wilkins's thoughts about the room.

a) What do lines 15-19 show about Mrs. Wilkins's feelings towards the room? Explain your answer using evidence from the text.

....

....

....

....

....

b) In line 20, Mrs. Wilkins describes the room as "so sweet", but also "like a cell". What is the effect of this? What might it suggest about her character?

....

....

....

....

....

Q4 The extract explores Mrs. Wilkins's surroundings.

a) Why do you think the writer chose to include a single word of speech on line 24?

....

....

b) How else is the extract structured to show Mrs. Wilkins's enjoyment of her surroundings? Give one other way.

....

....

....

....

....

Q5 In lines 25-33, the writer describes what Mrs. Wilkins can see and feel from her window.

a) What language technique is used to describe the sea and mountains in lines 25-27?

....

b) What effect does this create?

....

....

....

c) How else does the writer use language to describe Mrs. Wilkins's surroundings in lines 25-33? Write about the effect on the reader in your answer.

....

....

....

....

....

....

....

....

Q6 Mellersh is Mrs. Wilkins's husband. What impression do you get of her feelings towards him? How does the writer create this impression?

Q7 How does the writer create the feeling that Mrs. Wilkins is happier in Italy than in England? Give examples from the text.

You might want to think about:

- how the writer shows Mrs. Wilkins's feelings
- how Italy is described
- what the tone of the extract is.

Extension Activity

Mrs. Wilkins has travelled from England to stay in Italy. Write a diary entry about travelling in (or to) a new place. This can be somewhere you've been, or you can make it up. Think about how you can use language and tone to describe the place and your feelings about it to the reader.

Exercise C — Life of Pi

Abridged extract from Chapter 92

Canadian author Yann Martel's 2001 novel won the Man Booker Prize in 2002. The narrator, Pi, recounts how his family died after their ship, which also carried zoo animals, sank in a storm. Pi was left stranded on a lifeboat with a tiger. In this extract, Pi has been at sea for many months.

I made an exceptional botanical* discovery. But there will be many who disbelieve the following episode. Still, I give it to you now because it's part of the story and it happened to me.

I was on my side. It was an hour or two past noon on a day of quiet sunshine and gentle breeze. I had slept a short while, a diluted sleep that had brought no rest and no dreams. I turned over to my other side, expending as little energy as possible in doing so. I opened my eyes.

In the near distance I saw trees. I did not react. I was certain it was an illusion that a few blinks would make disappear.

The trees remained. In fact, they grew to be a forest. They were part of a low-lying island. I pushed myself up. I continued to disbelieve my eyes. But it was a thrill to be deluded in such a high-quality way. The trees were beautiful. They were like none I had ever seen before. They had a pale bark, and equally distributed branches that carried an amazing profusion* of leaves. These leaves were brilliantly green, a green so bright and emerald that, next to it, vegetation during the monsoons was drab olive.

I blinked deliberately, expecting my eyelids to act like lumberjacks. But the trees would not fall.

I looked down. I was both satisfied and disappointed with what I saw. The island had no soil. Not that the trees stood in water. Rather, they stood in what appeared to be a dense mass of vegetation, as sparkling green as the leaves. Who had ever heard of land with no soil? With trees growing out of pure vegetation? I felt satisfaction because such a geology confirmed that I was right, that this island was a chimera*, a play of the mind. By the same token I felt disappointment because an island, any island, however strange, would have been very good to come upon.

Since the trees continued to stand, I continued to look. To take in green, after so much blue, was like music to my eyes. Green is a lovely colour. It is the colour of Islam. It is my favourite colour.

After some minutes I crept up to the side of the boat. "Look for green," said the survival manual. Well, this was green. In fact, it was chlorophyll heaven. A green to outshine food colouring and flashing neon lights. A green to get drunk on. "Ultimately, a foot is the only good judge of land," pursued the manual. The island was within reach of a foot. To judge — and be disappointed — or not to judge, that was the question.

I decided to judge. I looked about to see if there were sharks. There were none. I turned on my stomach, and holding on to the tarpaulin, I slowly brought a leg down. My foot entered the sea. It was pleasingly cool. The island lay just a little further down, shimmering in the water. I stretched. I expected the bubble of illusion to burst at any second.

It did not. My foot sank into clear water and met the rubbery resistance of something flexible but solid. I put more weight down. The illusion would not give. I put my full weight on my foot. Still I did not sink. Still I did not believe.

Finally, it was my nose that was the judge of land. It came to my olfactory* sense, full and fresh, overwhelming: the smell of vegetation. I gasped. After months of nothing but salt-water-bleached smells, this reek of vegetable organic matter was intoxicating. It was then that I believed, and the only thing that sank was my mind; my thought process became disjointed. My leg began to shake.

"My God! My God!" I whimpered.

I fell overboard.

Glossary:
botanical — related to plants
profusion — a large amount
chimera — an unrealistic hope
olfactory — relating to the sense of smell

Q1 In paragraph one, how does the writer engage the reader's attention? Explain your answer.

....

....

....

....

....

Q2 Read lines 8-19. List four things about the island.

1. ....
2. ....
3. ....
4. ....

Q3 Pi comes across the island after spending a long time at sea.

a) Read line 13. How does this simile show Pi's reaction to the island?

....

....

....

....

b) Read lines 6-19. Do you think that Pi's descriptions of the island make it sound unusual? Give examples from the text to support your answer.

....

....

....

....

....

....

....

....

Q4 In lines 20-26, how does the writer use colour to describe the island? Use evidence from the text in your answer.

....

....

....

....

....

....

By the end of the novel, the reader is left with doubts over what truly happened to Pi when he was at sea. The tiger he was stranded with is nowhere to be found and Pi is the only person who knows the truth.

Q5 Circle the narrative viewpoint used in this extract and explain its effect.

first person	second person	third person

....

....

....

....

....

....

Q6 "The narrator seems unreliable in this extract." To what extent do you agree with this statement? Explain your answer using evidence from the text.

....

....

....

....

....

....

Q7 Read lines 31-38. How does the tone change in this part of the extract? Use evidence from the text in your answer.

Q8 This extract details Pi's experience of a new place. How is the extract structured to make the text interesting for the reader? What effect does this create?

You might want to think about:

- when the writer uses different types of sensory language
- how the extract starts, develops and ends
- where the writer has chosen to use different sentence types.

Extension Activity

Think of some other narrators in stories that you know. They don't have to be from a book — they could narrate in a film. Think about how their narrative voice affected the tone and the story's overall structure. What similarities and differences do they have with the narrator in this extract?

Exercise A — The Haunting of Hill House

Extract from Chapter 7

'The Haunting of Hill House', published in 1959, is a gothic horror novel written by Shirley Jackson. In the book, Eleanor, Theodora, Luke and a doctor investigate an old mansion for evidence of the supernatural. In this extract, they are hiding in a bedroom while an unseen force tries to get in. By the end of the book, Eleanor is believed to have been possessed by the spirits in the house.

"It can't get in," Theodora was whispering over and over, her eyes on the door, "it can't get in, don't let it get in, it can't get in — " The shaking stopped, the door was quiet, and a little caressing touch began on the doorknob, feeling intimately and softly and then, because the door was locked, patting and fondling the doorframe, as though wheedling to be let in.

"It knows we're here," Eleanor whispered, and Luke, looking back at her over his shoulder, gestured furiously for her to be quiet.

It is so cold, Eleanor thought childishly; I will never be able to sleep again with all this noise coming from inside my head; how can these others hear the noise when it is coming from inside my head? I am disappearing inch by inch into this house, I am going apart a little bit at a time because all this noise is breaking me; why are the *others* frightened?

She was aware, dully, that the pounding had begun again, the metallic overwhelming sound of it washed over her like waves; she put her cold hands to her mouth to feel if her face was still there; I have had enough, she thought, I am too cold.

"At the nursery door," Luke said tensely, speaking clearly through the noise. "At the nursery door; don't." And he put out a hand to stop the doctor.

"Purest love," Theodora said madly, "purest love." And she began to giggle again.

"If they don't open the doors — " Luke said to the doctor. The doctor stood now with his head against the door, listening, with Luke holding his arm to keep him from moving.

Now we are going to have a new noise, Eleanor thought, listening to the inside of her head; it is changing. The pounding had stopped, as though it had proved ineffectual, and there was now a swift movement up and down the hall, as of an animal pacing back and forth with unbelievable impatience, watching first one door and then another, alert for a movement inside, and there was again the little babbling murmur which Eleanor remembered; Am I doing it? she wondered quickly, is that me? And heard the tiny laughter beyond the door, mocking her.

"Fe-fi-fo-fum," Theodora said under her breath, and the laughter swelled and became a shouting; it's inside my head, Eleanor thought, putting her hands over her face, it's inside my head and it's getting out, getting out, getting out —

Now the house shivered and shook, the curtains dashing against the windows, the furniture swaying, and the noise in the hall became so great that it pushed against the walls; they could hear breaking glass as the pictures in the hall came down, and perhaps the smashing of windows. Luke and the doctor strained against the door, as though desperately holding it shut, and the floor moved under their feet. We're going, we're going, Eleanor thought, and heard Theodora say, far away, "The house is coming down." She sounded calm, and beyond fear. Holding to the bed, buffeted and shaken, Eleanor put her head down and closed her eyes and bit her lips against the cold and felt the sickening drop as the room fell away beneath her and then right itself and then turned, slowly, swinging.

Q1 The first paragraph focuses on the door the unseen force is trying to open. How does this paragraph make you feel and why?

....

....

....

....

Q2 The third paragraph deals with what Eleanor is thinking. How is Eleanor being affected by the supernatural force? Use evidence from the text in your answer.

....

....

....

....

....

Q3 The author describes sounds made by the unseen force throughout the extract.

a) How is language used to describe sound in lines 11-13? What effect does this have?

....

....

....

....

....

b) How is language used to describe sounds in lines 19-24? What effect does this have?

....

....

....

....

....

Q4 This extract has a third-person narrator, but in parts of the extract (e.g. lines 7-10) Eleanor narrates her thoughts in the first person. Why do you think the author does this?

Q5 The extract features a lot of repetition. What effect does this have? Use examples from the extract to explain your answer.

Q6 How has the author structured the extract to create a sense of fear in the reader?

Q7 "The author's descriptions of the characters contribute to how scary the extract is more than the descriptions of the supernatural threat." How far do you agree with this statement?

You might want to think about:

- how the characters and the supernatural threat are presented
- how the extract makes you feel and why
- what the overall tone of the extract is and how it is created.

Structure is important — make sure you can talk about it...

Writing about structure can be tricky, but there are lots of ways to go about it. Look at whether the focus of the extract changes from start to finish, or if the pace of the action speeds up or slows down. You can also talk about whether the tense or narrator changes, or how the paragraphs fit together.

Exercise B — The Island of Doctor Moreau

Adapted extract from Chapter 15

'The Island of Doctor Moreau' (1896) is by H.G. Wells. The novel's narrator, Edward Prendick, is rescued from a shipwreck and taken to an island inhabited by a scientist named Doctor Moreau and his assistant Montgomery. There, Prendick comes across strange half-man, half-animal creatures. Shortly before this extract, he learns that Moreau is trying to surgically turn animals into humans.

And here perhaps I may give a few general facts about the island and the Beast People. The island, which was of irregular outline and lay low upon the wide sea, had a total area, I suppose, of seven or eight square miles. It was volcanic in origin, and was now fringed on three sides by coral reefs; some fumaroles* to the northward, and a hot spring, were the only traces of the forces that had long since originated it. Now and then a faint quiver of earthquake would be noticeable, and sometimes the ascent of the spire of smoke would be rendered tumultuous by gusts of steam; but that was all. The population of the island, Montgomery informed me, now numbered rather more than sixty of these strange creations of Moreau's art, not counting the smaller monstrosities which lived in the undergrowth and were without human form. Altogether he had made nearly a hundred and twenty; but many had died, and others — like the writhing Footless Thing of which he had told me — had come by violent ends.

It would be impossible for me to describe these Beast People in detail; my eye has had no training in details, and unhappily I cannot sketch. Most striking, perhaps, in their general appearance was the disproportion between the legs of these creatures and the length of their bodies; and yet — so relative is our idea of grace — my eye became habituated* to their forms, and at last I even fell in with their persuasion that my own long thighs were ungainly.

The two most formidable Animal Men were my Leopard-man and a creature made of hyena and swine. Larger than these were the three bull-creatures who pulled in the boat. There were three Swine-men and a Swine-woman, a mare-rhinoceros-creature, and several other females whose sources I did not ascertain. There were several wolf-creatures, a bear-bull, and a Saint-Bernard-man. I have already described the Ape-man, and there was a particularly hateful (and evil-smelling) old woman made of vixen and bear, whom I hated from the beginning. Smaller creatures were certain dappled youths and my little sloth-creature. But enough of this catalogue.

At first I had a shivering horror of the brutes, felt all too keenly that they were still brutes; but insensibly I became a little habituated to the idea of them, and moreover I was affected by Montgomery's attitude towards them. He had been with them so long that he had come to regard them as almost normal human beings. His London days seemed a glorious, impossible past to him. Only once in a year or so did he go to Arica* to deal with Moreau's agent, a trader in animals there. He hardly met the finest type of mankind in that seafaring village. The men aboard-ship, he told me, seemed at first just as strange to him as the Beast Men seemed to me, — unnaturally long in the leg, flat in the face, prominent in the forehead, suspicious, dangerous, and cold-hearted. In fact, he did not like men: his heart had warmed to me, he thought, because he had saved my life. I fancied even then that he had a sneaking kindness for some of these metamorphosed brutes, a vicious sympathy with some of their ways, but that he attempted to veil it from me at first.

I say I became habituated to the Beast People, that a thousand things which had seemed unnatural and repulsive speedily became natural and ordinary to me. I would see one of the clumsy bovine*-creatures who worked the launch treading heavily through the undergrowth, and find myself asking, trying hard to recall, how he differed from some really human yokel* trudging home from his mechanical labours; or I would meet the Fox-bear woman's vulpine*, shifty face, strangely human in its speculative cunning, and even imagine I had met it before in some city byway.

Glossary:
fumaroles — holes in the earth's surface that release volcanic steam and gases
habituated — familiar with
Arica — a city in Chile
bovine — relating to cattle
yokel — a person from the countryside who is thought to be unsophisticated
vulpine — relating to foxes

Q1 Read the extract. Tick the two statements below which are TRUE.

a) The island is over 100 square miles in area. ☐

b) Nearly all of Moreau's creations have been a success. ☐

c) The Beast People tend to have limbs which are short compared to their bodies. ☐

d) The Beast People think that Prendick looks graceful. ☐

e) The Beast People are made from a wide variety of different animals. ☐

f) Montgomery can't remember what his life in London used to be like. ☐

g) Montgomery disapproves of the Beast People's animalistic behaviour. ☐

Q2 Lines 1-6 describe the island. In your own words, briefly explain what the island is like.

....

....

....

....

....

Q3 The third paragraph focuses on the creatures that Prendick sees.

a) What is meant by the phrase "The two most formidable Animal Men" (line 16)?

....

....

b) Why do you think the author lists the Beast People in this paragraph?
What effect does it have on the reader?

....

....

....

....

....

....

Q4 What impression do you get of Montgomery in this extract? Explain your answer.

....

....

....

....

....

....

....

Q5 How is the extract structured to reveal information about the Beast People?

....

....

....

....

....

....

....

Q6 Prendick says it's "impossible" for him to describe the Beast People "in detail".
What effect does the lack of detailed descriptions of the Beast People have on the reader?

....

....

....

....

....

....

....

Q7 How do Prendick's feelings towards the Beast People change? Use examples from the extract to support your opinions.

You might want to think about:

- how language is used to describe the Beast People
- which methods are used to express Prendick's feelings
- what the tone of the extract is.

Extension Activity

RESEARCH TASK

Humans taking scientific experiments too far has proved to be a popular theme in stories over the years. Note down some examples from books, films or television. What sort of experiments were carried out? What was the aim of these experiments and how did characters react to them? Are there any similarities between 'The Island of Doctor Moreau' and these other stories?

Exercise C — The Haunting of Alaizabel Cray

Extract from Chapter 20

'The Haunting of Alaizabel Cray' was written by Chris Wooding and published in 2001. It features a young man named Thaniel Fox who hunts monsters known as wych-kin. In this extract, the wych-kin are about to unleash a violent attack on London which will leave the city overrun.

The catastrophe came slowly on to London. Morning had broken, sheeting rain down on to the dirty streets, turning everything dark and glistening. People got up as usual; the tram drivers, the muffin-men*, the cobblers and solicitors. The night-folk took their rest, the prostitutes and the gamblers and those who ran the opium dens* in the Docklands. One shift off, one shift on, the city went on as normal, unaware of the horror bearing down upon it. Only the innocent and the sensitive felt what was happening. All across London, babies cried incessantly. Palm-readers and fortune-tellers — those who were genuine, anyway — shut up their shops and huddled fearfully in their homes. Dogs howled, cats wailed, and people commented that it was most odd, how, even in the centre of the city, the cacophony of animals was to be heard in the distance.

It was in Margate that people noticed it first. There was a stiff west-to-east breeze blowing, curving the rain as it fell. Why, then, was the high, bobbled blanket of cloud moving west, *against* the wind — towards London? Similar observations were made in the north and south, where the clouds were rolling perpendicular* to the bluster, crawling steadily inward in the direction of the capital.

The storm began at mid-afternoon, doubling the fury of the rain and jabbing forked sparks of lightning down on the city, the sky flashing and booming with terrible rage. So heavy was the downpour that it masked the clouds above, and consequently few were aware that the thick grey mass looming over them had begun to slowly circle.

So immense was the scale of the phenomenon that it would only have been possible to fully appreciate it from high above. If a person could have ridden a hot-air balloon high into the stratosphere, higher than anyone had ever gone, they might have looked down and seen a sight never seen before. The British Isles were covered in cloud, as was usual for this time of year, but never had it behaved in such a way. It appeared that London was sucking in the cloud in a great spiral. The vast, louring* bulk was circling massively, like water down a plughole. London was the centre of a huge, rotating monstrosity of cloud. The eye of the hurricane.

By now it was only the most ignorant or those best versed in denial of the unknown that could not feel the unease and faint dread which settled upon them like ash. Something primal in their souls spoke to them, telling them that something unnatural was happening, made their spines prickle and their hands jitter. Only the women discussed their fears; the men kept it to themselves. That was the way of things.

The gas lamps were lit at four o'clock, so dark had it become. They glowed pallidly, reflecting in waving lines on the rippling rivers that chased each other down the streets. By six o'clock, people had begun noticing the reddish glow from the sky, strongest in the south, across the Thames; but the rain was still too strong to see through.

Just shy of eight o'clock, the rain thinned and stopped; and finally, the people of London realised that their unease had not been mere fancy, but terribly real. For there, hanging above the Old Quarter, was the centre of the spiral of cloud that stretched across the land, and at its core the sky glowed a foul arterial* red. Like a slow whirlpool of blood it stirred around and around, rumbling and growling, flickers of dry lightning lashing from the maelstrom* and darting down to the ruined, bomb-torn streets below.

Behind the clouds, night fell, deepening the already dark day to black. The fog gathered in the alleys and roiled* out on to the streets.

Glossary:
muffin-men — men who went door-to-door delivering fresh bread in the 19th and early 20th centuries
opium dens — places where opium, a drug, was sold
perpendicular — at a 90° angle to something else
louring — dark and threatening
arterial — relating to blood vessels which carry blood from the heart to the rest of the body
maelstrom — a whirlpool, or a violent / chaotic situation
roiled — moved in an unstable, swirling way

This novel is set in an alternate version of Victorian London. Elements of the novel's setting are recognisable as 19th-century England, but it is also a very different world.

Q1 What impression do you get of this fictional London from the first paragraph and why?

Q2 The weather plays a significant part in this extract.

a) The weather is personified in paragraphs 2 and 3. Give three examples of this.

1.

2.

3.

b) What is the effect of this personification?
Use the examples you gave above to explain your response.

Q3 Find a simile from lines 18-40 and explain how it affects the reader.

Q4 How is the extract structured to guide the reader through the development of the storm?

....

....

....

....

....

....

....

....

Q5 The author creates tension in different ways in this extract.

a) How does the author use structure to help create tension?

....

....

....

....

....

b) How do the author's descriptions of people help to create tension? Give examples from the extract.

....

....

....

....

....

....

....

....

....

Q6 "The author effectively makes the approaching storm sound supernatural and threatening." How far do you agree with this statement?

You might want to think about:

- how language is used to describe the storm and the city
- what the tone of the extract is
- how the extract makes you feel.

Extension Activity

Effective descriptions are important in presenting a clear image to the reader. Write a description of something from your imagination — this could be an animal, a person, a building or anything else. Swap with a friend and try to draw what they described. How close is your drawing to your friend's creative vision? What kind of language most helped you visualise their ideas?

Exercise A — The Tiger's Wife

Extract from the start of the prologue

This novel was written by Téa Obreht and was published in 2011. It tells the story of a woman's relationship with her grandfather and her efforts to understand the circumstances surrounding his death. In this extract, the narrator remembers going with her grandfather to the zoo as a child.

In my earliest memory, my grandfather is bald as a stone and he takes me to see the tigers. He puts on his hat, his big-buttoned raincoat, and I wear my lacquered* shoes and velvet dress. It is autumn, and I am four years old. The certainty of this process: my grandfather's hand, the bright hiss of the trolley*, the dampness of the morning, the crowded walk up the hill to the citadel* park. Always in my grandfather's breast pocket: *The Jungle Book*, with its gold-leaf cover and old yellow pages. I am not allowed to hold it, but it will stay open on his knee all afternoon while he recites the passages to me. Even though my grandfather is not wearing his stethoscope or white coat, the lady at the ticket counter in the entrance shed calls him "Doctor".

Then there is the popcorn cart, the umbrella stand, a small kiosk with postcards and pictures. Down the stairs and past the aviary where the sharp-eared owls sleep, through the garden that runs the length of the citadel wall, framed with cages. Once there was a king here, a sultan, his Janissaries*. Now the cannon windows facing the street hold blocked-off troughs filled with tepid water. The cage bars curve out, rusted orange. In his free hand, my grandfather is carrying a blue bag my grandma has prepared for us. In it: six-day-old cabbage heads for the hippopotamus, carrots and celery for the sheep and deer and the bull moose, who is a kind of phenomenon. In his pocket, my grandfather has hidden some sugar cubes for the pony that pulls the park carriage. I will not remember this as sentimentality, but as greatness.

The tigers live in the outer moat of the fortress. We climb the castle stairs, past the waterbirds and the sweating windows of the monkey house, past the wolf growing his winter coat. We pass the bearded vultures and then the bears, asleep all day, smelling of damp earth and the death of something. My grandfather picks me up and props my feet against the handrail so I can look down and see the tigers in the moat.

My grandfather never refers to the tiger's wife by name. His arm is around me and my feet are on the handrail, and my grandfather might say, "I once knew a girl who loved tigers so much she almost became one herself." Because I am little, and my love of tigers comes directly from him, I believe he is talking about me, offering me a fairy tale in which I can imagine myself — and will, for years and years.

The cages face a courtyard, and we go down the stairs and walk slowly from cage to cage. There is a panther, too, ghost spots paling his oil-slick coat; a sleepy, bloated lion from Africa. But the tigers are awake and livid, bright with rancor*. Stripe-lashed shoulders rolling, they flank one another up and down the narrow causeway of rock, and the smell of them is sour and warm and fills everything. It will stay with me the whole day, even after I have had my bath and gone to bed, and will return at random times: at school, at a friend's birthday party, even years later, at the pathology* lab, or on the drive home from Galina.

Glossary:
lacquered — covered in a shiny, glossy finish
trolley — a form of transportation, similar to a tram
citadel — a castle/fortress in or near a city
Janissaries — soldiers/bodyguards in the Ottoman (Turkish) empire
rancor — a feeling of resentment and anger
pathology — a type of science focused on diseases

Q1 The extract describes the narrator's grandfather.

a) Write down four things the reader learns about the grandfather in the first paragraph.

1. ....

2. ....

3. ....

4. ....

b) Read lines 13-29. What do the grandfather's actions in this part of the text suggest about his personality? Give evidence from the text in your answer.

....

....

....

....

Q2 "The first paragraph gives a clear sense of the relationship between the grandfather and his grandchild." Do you agree with this? Explain your answer.

....

....

....

....

....

Sultans were the rulers of the Ottoman Empire, while Janissaries were soldiers who were known for their discipline and loyalty to the Sultan. The Ottoman Empire existed between the 14th and early 20th centuries. It controlled large parts of Asia, Africa and Europe, including the Balkans (a region in south-eastern Europe), where this novel is set.

Q3 In line 11, the writer says "Once there was a king here, a sultan, his Janissaries."
Why do you think the writer has chosen to mention this? What effect does it have on the reader?

....

....

....

....

Q4 In this extract, the writer describes a childhood memory. How has the writer structured the extract to describe this memory? What effect does this structure have on the reader?

....

....

....

....

....

....

....

Q5 What effect does the writer's choice of tense have on the reader?

....

....

....

....

....

'The Tiger's Wife' can be described as containing elements of a genre called 'magical realism'. This means that it combines a realistic portrayal of the world with superstition, fantasy and myth.

Q6 Find an example from the text that suggests this is a magical realist novel. Explain your answer.

....

....

....

....

....

....

Q7 "The writer's use of sensory language brings the narrator's memories to life." Do you agree with this statement? Explain your answer.

You might want to think about:

- how sensory language is used to describe animals
- how sensory language is used to present the settings
- how sensory language is used to present the narrator's grandfather.

Extension Activity

The relationship between humans and animals has often been explored, e.g. in books, television programmes and films. Note down any other examples of stories about humans and animals that you can think of. Think about how this dynamic is shown in different stories — what are the similarities and differences between those relationships and the relationship in this extract?

Exercise B — The Little Stranger

Extract from the beginning of Chapter 1

'The Little Stranger', written by Sarah Waters, was published in 2009. Set in the 1940s, it is a ghost story about the Ayres family, who live in a large house called Hundreds Hall. The narrator is a doctor who is called to the house. In this extract he remembers going to Hundreds Hall as a boy.

I first saw Hundreds Hall when I was ten years old. It was the summer after the war, and the Ayreses still had most of their money then, were still big people in the district. The event was an Empire Day* fête: I stood with a line of other village children making a Boy Scout salute while Mrs Ayres and the Colonel went past us, handing out commemorative medals; afterwards we sat to tea with our parents at long tables on what I suppose was the south lawn. Mrs Ayres would have been twenty-four or -five, her husband a few years older; their little girl, Susan, would have been about six. They must have made a very handsome family, but my memory of them is vague. I recall most vividly the house itself, which struck me as an absolute mansion. I remember its lovely ageing details: the worn red brick, the cockled* window glass, the weathered sandstone edgings. They made it look blurred and slightly uncertain — like an ice, I thought, just beginning to melt in the sun.

There were no trips inside, of course. The doors and French windows stood open, but each had a rope or a ribbon tied across it; the lavatories set aside for our use were the grooms' and the gardeners', in the stable block. My mother, however, still had friends among the servants, and when the tea was finished and people were given the run of the grounds, she took me quietly into the house by a side door, and we spent a little time with the cook and the kitchen girls. The visit impressed me terribly. The kitchen was a basement one, reached by a cool vaulted corridor with something of the feel of a castle dungeon. An extraordinary number of people seemed to be coming and going along it with hampers and trays. The girls had such a mountain of crockery to wash, my mother rolled up her sleeves to help them; and to my very great delight, as a reward for her labour I was allowed to take my pick of the jellies and 'shapes' that had come back uneaten from the fête. I was put to sit at a deal-topped table*, and given a spoon from the family's own drawer — a heavy thing of dulled silver, its bowl almost bigger than my mouth.

But then came an even greater treat. High up on the wall of the vaulted passage was a junction-box of wires and bells, and when one of these bells was set ringing, calling the parlourmaid upstairs, she took me with her, so that I might peep past the green baize* curtain that separated the front of the house from the back. I could stand and wait for her there, she said, if I was very good and quiet. I must only be sure to keep behind the curtain, for if the Colonel or the missus were to see me, there'd be a row.

I was an obedient child, as a rule. But the curtain opened onto the corner junction of two marble-floored passages, each one filled with marvellous things; and once she had disappeared softly in one direction, I took a few daring steps in the other. The thrill of it was astonishing. I don't mean the simple thrill of trespass, I mean the thrill of the house itself, which came to me from every surface — from the polish on the floor, the patina* on wooden chairs and cabinets, the bevel* of a looking-glass, the scroll of a frame. I was drawn to one of the dustless white walls, which had a decorative plaster border, a representation of acorns and leaves. I had never seen anything like it, outside of a church, and after a second of looking it over I did what strikes me now as a dreadful thing: I worked my fingers around one of the acorns and tried to prise it from its setting; and when that failed to release it, I got out my penknife and dug away with that. I didn't do it in a spirit of vandalism. I wasn't a spiteful or destructive boy. It was simply that, in admiring the house, I wanted to possess a piece of it — or rather, as if the admiration itself, which I suspected a more ordinary child would not have felt, entitled me to it. I was like a man, I suppose, wanting a lock of hair from the head of a girl he had suddenly and blindingly become enamoured of.

Glossary:
Empire Day — a day celebrating the British Empire
cockled — wrinkled
deal-topped table — a table topped with soft wood, e.g. pine
baize — coarse material
patina — shininess that develops on old wooden objects
bevel — a sloping surface

Q1 In the extract, the narrator describes the Ayres family.

a) Summarise what we learn about the Ayres family in the first paragraph.

b) What is your impression of the Ayres family in the extract as a whole? What gives you this impression?

Empire Day was first celebrated in 1902 and became a major annual event. People would gather up and down the country for speeches, songs, marches and parties. It was renamed Commonwealth Day in the 1950s, and although it is still celebrated today, the decline of the British Empire over time has meant it isn't celebrated as much anymore.

Q2 Why do you think the writer chose to set the visit to Hundreds Hall on Empire Day? How does this relate to the Ayres family?

Q3 In the final paragraph, the narrator describes how he tried to take a decorative acorn from Hundreds Hall.

a) Explain the reasons the narrator gives for trying to take the acorn.

b) What effect does this incident have on how the reader sees the narrator's character?

Q4 Compare the presentation of the servant's quarters and the rest of Hundreds Hall. How does the writer use language to present these two sides of Hundreds Hall?

Q5 The narrator is speaking from the 1940s, but these events took place a long time before that. How can you tell from the extract that the narrator is describing memories from a long time in his past?

Q6 "The narrator's memory of Hundreds Hall seems important to him. He is clearly interested in the house and the people who live and work there." To what extent do you agree with this statement?

You might want to think about:

- how language is used to describe Hundreds Hall
- how the structure shows the narrator's interest in different parts of Hundreds Hall
- how the tone of the extract reflects the narrator's feelings about Hundreds Hall.

Extension Activity

The narrator of 'The Little Stranger' was very impressed by his first visit to Hundreds Hall. Think of something you have admired, been captivated by or felt a longing for. Write a few paragraphs about it, describing it using language which shows the reader how strongly you feel.

Exercise C — The Fishermen

Extract from Chapter 1

This extract is from Chigozie Obioma's debut novel, published in 2015. It is centred around a family living in Akure, Nigeria in the 1990s. The narrator is one of six siblings who later become fishermen. In this extract, the narrator describes the day his father had to move away from home.

"I will start living in Yola from today onwards, and I don't want you boys to give your mother any troubles." His face contorted when he said this, the way it did whenever he wanted to drive the hounds of fear into us. He spoke slowly, his voice deeper and louder, every word tacked nine inches deep into the beams of our minds. So that, if we went ahead and disobeyed, he would make us conjure the exact moment he gave us the instruction in its complete detail with the simple phrase, "I told you."

"I will call her regularly, and if I hear any bad news" — he struck his forefinger aloft to fortify his words — "I mean, any funny acts at all, I'll give you the Guerdon* for them."

He'd said the word "Guerdon" — a word with which he emphasized a warning or highlighted the retribution for a wrong act — with so much vigour that veins bulged at both sides of his face. This word, once pronounced, often completed the message. He brought out two twenty-naira notes* from the breast pocket of his coat and dropped them on our study table.

"For both of you," he said, and left the room.

Obembe and I were still sitting in our bed trying to make sense of all that when we heard Mother speaking to him outside the house in a voice so loud it seemed he was already far away.

"Eme, remember you have growing boys back here," she'd said. "I'm telling you, oh."

She was still speaking when Father started his Peugeot 504. At the sound of it, Obembe and I hurried from our room, but Father was already driving out of the gate. He was gone.

Whenever I think of our story, how that morning would mark the last time we'd live together, all of us, as the family we'd always been, I begin — even these two decades later — to wish he hadn't left, that he had never received that transfer letter. Before that letter came, everything was in place: Father went to work every morning and Mother, who ran a fresh food store in the open market, tended to my five siblings and me who, like the children of most families in Akure, went to school. Everything followed its natural course. We gave little thought to past events. Time meant nothing back then. The days came with clouds hanging in the sky filled with cupfuls of dust in the dry seasons, and the sun lasting into the night. It was as if a hand drew hazy pictures in the sky during the rainy seasons, when rain fell in deluges pulsating with spasms of thunderstorms for six uninterrupted months. Because things followed this known and structured pattern, no day was worthy of remembrance. All that mattered was the present and the foreseeable future. Glimpses of it mostly came like a locomotive train treading tracks of hope, with black coal in its heart and a loud elephantine toot. Sometimes these glimpses came through dreams or flights of fanciful thoughts that whispered in your head — *I will be a pilot, or the president of Nigeria, rich man, own helicopters* — for the future was what we made of it. It was a blank canvas on which anything could be imagined. But Father's move to Yola changed the equation of things: time and seasons and the past began to matter, and we started to yearn and crave for it even more than the present and the future.

Glossary:
Guerdon — an old-fashioned word for reward, but here the father means a punishment
twenty-naira notes — Nigerian currency

Akure, the town the family live in, is in south-western Nigeria. The father is sent by his employers to work in Yola, which is in eastern Nigeria. The two places are around 1000 kilometres (600 miles) apart.

Q1 Read lines 1-17 of the extract. What impression do you get of the father from the writer's description of him? Write about Obioma's use of language in your answer.

....

....

....

....

....

....

....

Q2 The narrator's mother is also present in this extract.

a) Find an example of how the narrator's mother is presented from lines 13-17. Explain its effect.

....

....

....

b) Find an example of how the narrator's mother is presented from lines 20-23. Explain its effect.

....

....

....

c) "The narrator's mother isn't important in this extract."
Do you agree with this statement? Refer to the text in your answer.

....

....

....

....

Q3 In the last paragraph of the extract, the narrator talks about his attitude towards the past, present and future.

a) Summarise how the narrator felt about the past before and after his father left.

....

....

....

....

b) How is language used to describe the narrator's attitude to the future before his father left?

....

....

....

....

....

....

....

....

Q4 The events in this extract had a big impact on the narrator. How does the structure of the extract reflect this?

....

....

....

....

....

....

....

Q5 How does the writer present the narrator's life and experiences?

You might want to think about:

- the language the writer uses to present the narrator's life and experiences
- how the extract starts, develops and ends
- the overall tone and style of the extract.

....

....

....

....

....

....

....

....

....

....

....

....

....

....

....

....

....

....

....

....

....

Don't just read the extract once...

When you first get your hands on an extract, it's a good idea to read it through more than once. The first read-through should be for getting your head around what the text is all about — think about what the plot is, who the characters are and where or when it might be set. For the next reading, you can start thinking about how the text is written, picking out key features of the extract's language, tone and structure.

Exercise A — Larry's Party

Extract from the beginning of Chapter 1

'Larry's Party' (1997) is by Carol Shields. It tells the story of an ordinary Canadian man named Larry Weller by describing episodes of his life over a twenty-year period. This extract sees Larry realise that he accidentally picked up someone else's jacket in a coffee shop as he left to see his girlfriend, Dorrie.

By mistake Larry Weller took someone else's Harris tweed* jacket instead of his own, and it wasn't till he jammed his hand in the pocket that he knew something was wrong.

His hand was traveling straight into a silky void. His five fingers pushed down, looking for the balled-up Kleenex* from his own familiar worn-out pocket, the nickels and dimes, the ticket receipts from all the movies he and Dorrie had been seeing lately. Also those hard little bits of lint, like meteor grit, that never seem to lose themselves once they've worked into the seams.

This pocket — today's pocket — was different. Clean, a slippery valley. The stitches he touched at the bottom weren't his stitches. His fingertips glided now on a sweet little sea of lining. He grabbed for the buttons. Leather, the real thing. And something else — the sleeves were a good half inch longer than they should have been.

This jacket was twice the value of his own. The texture, the seams. You could see it got sent all the time to the cleaners. Another thing, you could tell by the way the shoulders sprang out that this jacket got parked on a thick wooden hanger at night. Above a row of polished shoes. Refilling its tweedy warp and woof* with oxygenated air.

He should have run back to the coffee shop to see if his own jacket was still scrunched there on the back of his chair, but it was already quarter to six, and Dorrie was expecting him at six sharp, and it was rush hour and he wasn't anywhere near the bus stop.

And — the thought came to him — what's the point? A jacket's a jacket. A person who patronizes* a place like Cafe Capri is almost asking to get his jacket copped. This way all that's happened is a kind of exchange.

Forget the bus, he decided. He'd walk. He'd stroll. In his hot new Harris tweed apparel. He'd push his shoulders along, letting them roll loose in their sockets. Forward with the right shoulder, bam, then the left shoulder coming up from behind. He'd let his arms swing wide. Fan his fingers out. Here comes the Big Guy, watch out for the Big Guy.

The sleeves rubbed light across the back of his hands, scratchy but not *too* scratchy.

And then he saw that the cuff buttons were leather too, a smaller-size version of the main buttons, but the same design, a sort of cross-pattern like a pecan pie cut in quarters, only the slices overlapped this little bit. You could feel the raised design with your finger, the way the four quadrants of leather crossed over and over each other, their edges cut wavy on the inside margin. These waves intersected in the middle, dived down there in a dark center and disappeared. A black hole in the button universe. Zero.

Quadrant was a word Larry hadn't even thought of for about ten years, not since geometry class, grade eleven.

The color of the jacket was mixed shades of brown, a strong background of freckled tobacco tones with subtle orange flecks. Very subtle. No one would say: hey, here comes this person with orange flecks distributed across his jacket. You'd have to be one inch away before you took in those flecks.

Glossary:
Harris tweed — a brand of high-quality woollen fabric made in Scotland
Kleenex — a brand of tissue
warp and woof — the horizontal and vertical threads which make up woven fabric
patronizes — is a customer of

Q1 The extract uses lots of descriptive language to describe the two jackets.

a) Give three examples from the extract where a simile or metaphor has been used to describe one of the jackets. Explain the effect each one has on the reader.

1. ....

....

....

....

2. ....

....

....

....

3. ....

....

....

....

b) How else is language used to describe the jackets? What effect does this have? Use examples from the extract to support your points.

....

....

....

....

....

....

....

....

....

....

....

Q2 "The writer should have described the setting and the rest of Larry's appearance in more detail instead of focusing on the jacket." How far do you agree with this statement? Why?

Q3 How is the extract structured to interest you as a reader?

Q4 The extract gives you an insight into the life of its main character, Larry. How does the language of the extract help the reader to understand Larry's thoughts and personality?

You might want to think about:

- how Larry's character is developed in the extract
- the style and tone of the extract
- the narrative viewpoint used in the extract.

Extension Activity

Think about all the different outfits you wear — for school, for socialising with friends and family, for playing sport or for relaxing at home. Write a description of each of these outfits, including how they look and how they make you feel when you wear them. Does the language you use change depending on the type of clothes you are writing about? How? Why do you think this is?

Exercise B — The Picture of Dorian Gray

Abridged extract from Chapter 7

'The Picture of Dorian Gray' is Oscar Wilde's only novel, although he wrote many plays, poems and short stories. It features a young, handsome pleasure-seeker (Dorian) who wishes that a portrait of himself would experience the effects of age and sin instead of his real body. In this extract, Dorian notices a change in his portrait after cruelly rejecting Sibyl Vane, a woman he said he loved.

In the huge gilt Venetian lantern that hung from the ceiling of the great, oak-panelled hall of entrance, lights were still burning from three flickering jets: thin blue petals of flame they seemed, rimmed with white fire. He turned them out and, having thrown his hat and cape on the table, passed through the library towards the door of his bedroom, a large octagonal chamber on the ground floor that, in his new-born feeling for luxury, he had just had decorated for himself and hung with some curious Renaissance tapestries that had been discovered stored in a disused attic at Selby Royal. As he was turning the handle of the door, his eye fell upon the portrait Basil Hallward had painted of him. He started back as if in surprise. Then he went on into his own room, looking somewhat puzzled. After he had taken the button-hole out of his coat, he seemed to hesitate. Finally, he came back, went over to the picture, and examined it. In the dim arrested light that struggled through the cream-coloured silk blinds, the face appeared to him to be a little changed. The expression looked different. One would have said that there was a touch of cruelty in the mouth. It was certainly strange.

He turned round and, walking to the window, drew up the blind. The bright dawn flooded the room and swept the fantastic shadows into dusky corners, where they lay shuddering. But the strange expression that he had noticed in the face of the portrait seemed to linger there, to be more intensified even. The quivering ardent* sunlight showed him the lines of cruelty round the mouth as clearly as if he had been looking into a mirror after he had done some dreadful thing.

He rubbed his eyes, and came close to the picture, and examined it again. There were no signs of any change when he looked into the actual painting, and yet there was no doubt that the whole expression had altered. It was not a mere fancy of his own. The thing was horribly apparent.

He threw himself into a chair and began to think. Suddenly there flashed across his mind what he had said in Basil Hallward's studio the day the picture had been finished. Yes, he remembered it perfectly. He had uttered a mad wish that he himself might remain young, and the portrait grow old; that his own beauty might be untarnished, and the face on the canvas bear the burden of his passions and his sins; that the painted image might be seared* with the lines of suffering and thought, and that he might keep all the delicate bloom and loveliness of his then just conscious boyhood. Surely his wish had not been fulfilled? Such things were impossible. It seemed monstrous even to think of them. And, yet, there was the picture before him, with the touch of cruelty in the mouth.

Cruelty! Had he been cruel? It was the girl's fault, not his. He had dreamed of her as a great artist, had given his love to her because he had thought her great. Then she had disappointed him. She had been shallow and unworthy. Why should he trouble about Sibyl Vane? She was nothing to him now.

But the picture? What was he to say of that? It held the secret of his life, and told his story. It had taught him to love his own beauty. Would it teach him to loathe his own soul? Would he ever look at it again?

No; it was merely an illusion wrought* on the troubled senses. The horrible night that he had passed had left phantoms behind it. Suddenly there had fallen upon his brain that tiny scarlet speck that makes men mad. The picture had not changed. It was folly* to think so.

Glossary:
ardent — burning or passionate
seared — scorched with heat
wrought — made or shaped
folly — foolish

Q1 The first paragraph describes Dorian's surroundings.
List four things you learn about his bedroom in lines 1-6.

1. ....

2. ....

3. ....

4. ....

Q2 How is language used to describe light in the first two paragraphs?
Give at least two examples and explain their effects.

....

Q3 How does Wilde convey Dorian's thoughts and feelings about Sybil to the reader? Use evidence from the text in your answer.

....

Q4 Describe the overall tone of the extract. Use evidence from the text in your answer.

....

....

....

....

....

....

....

....

....

....

Q5 "The portrait of Dorian is an important focus of this extract. The writer has structured the text to focus the reader's attention on the portrait." Do you agree with this statement? Why or why not?

....

....

....

....

....

....

....

....

....

....

....

....

....

....

Q6 How does the writer show Dorian's attitude towards the painting throughout the extract?

You might want to think about:

- how Dorian's thoughts and behaviour change throughout the extract
- how the structure of the extract reflects Dorian's feelings
- how language is used to show Dorian's attitude.

Extension Activity

Research other stories about wishes coming true. They might be from other novels, poems, films, songs or any other type of media. Look for patterns in the narratives — do wishes tend to be for good or for evil? What might the messages of these stories be? What are the similarities and differences between the wishes made in these stories and in 'The Picture of Dorian Gray'?

Exercise C — Norwegian Wood

Extract from Chapter 1

This extract is from Jay Rubin's English translation of Haruki Murakami's original novel, which is written in Japanese and was first published in 1987. The narrator of the text is Toru Watanabe, an adult who gives an account of his college days in Tokyo in the late 1960s. In this extract, Watanabe is reminded of his former relationship with a girl called Naoko, who later died.

Eighteen years have gone by, and still I can bring back every detail of that day in the meadow. Washed clean of summer's dust by days of gentle rain, the mountains wore a deep, brilliant green. The October breeze set white fronds* of head-high grasses swaying. One long streak of cloud hung pasted across a dome of frozen blue. It almost hurt to look at that far-off sky. A puff of wind swept across the meadow and through her hair before it slipped into the woods to rustle branches and send back snatches of distant barking — a hazy sound that seemed to reach us from the doorway to another world. We heard no other sounds. We met no other people. We saw only two bright red birds leap startled from the centre of the meadow and dart into the woods. As we ambled along, Naoko spoke to me of wells.

Memory is a funny thing. When I was in the scene I hardly paid it any attention. I never stopped to think of it as something that would make a lasting impression, certainly never imagined that 18 years later I would recall it in such detail. I didn't give a damn about the scenery that day. I was thinking about myself. I was thinking about the beautiful girl walking next to me. I was thinking about the two of us together, and then about myself again. I was at that age, that time of life when every sight, every feeling, every thought came back, like a boomerang, to me. And worse, I was in love. Love with complications. Scenery was the last thing on my mind.

Now, though, that meadow scene is the first thing that comes back to me. The smell of the grass, the faint chill of the wind, the line of the hills, the barking of a dog: these are the first things, and they come with absolute clarity. I feel as if I can reach out and trace them with a fingertip. And yet, as clear as the scene may be, no one is in it. No one. Naoko is not there, and neither am I. Where could we have disappeared to? How could such a thing have happened? Everything that seemed so important back then — Naoko, and the self I was then, and the world I had then: where could they have all gone? It's true, I can't even bring back her face — not straight away, at least. All I'm left holding is a background, pure scenery, with no people at the front.

True, given time enough, I can remember her face. I start joining images — her tiny, cold hand; her straight, black hair so smooth and cool to the touch; a soft, rounded earlobe and the microscopic mole just beneath it; the camel-hair coat she wore in the winter; her habit of looking straight into my eyes when asking a question; the slight trembling that would come to her voice now and then (as though she were speaking on a windy hilltop) — and suddenly her face is there, always in profile at first, because Naoko and I were always out walking together, side by side. Then she turns to me and smiles, and tilts her head just a little, and begins to speak, and she looks into my eyes as if trying to catch the image of a minnow that has darted across the pool of a limpid* spring.

Glossary:
fronds — long, thin leaves
limpid — crystal clear

Q1 In the first paragraph, Watanabe recalls walking with Naoko in a meadow 18 years ago. List four things that Watanabe saw while walking in the meadow in lines 1-8.

1. ....

2. ....

3. ....

4. ....

Q2 In the first paragraph, how does the writer create the impression that the narrator vividly remembers the meadow scene?

....

....

....

....

....

....

....

....

Q3 In the second paragraph, the narrator describes what he was like 18 years ago. How does the writer use language to show what the narrator was like as a young man? What is the effect of this?

....

....

....

....

....

....

....

....

Q4 Think about the structure of the extract. How has the writer used structure to keep the reader interested?

....

....

....

....

....

....

....

....

....

....

....

Q5 Why do you think the writer chooses to describe Naoko in the way that he does?

....

....

....

....

....

....

....

....

....

....

....

Q6 "The character of Watanabe seems to be in despair. He is obviously still in love with Naoko and wishes that he could still be with her." To what extent do you agree with this statement?

You might want to think about:

- what the overall tone of the extract is
- what the extract focuses on
- how the writer presents Watanabe.

Watch your tone...

Because the tone of a text is the feeling the words are written with, it can be hard to describe. The best way to figure it out is to look at the language of the text. Informal language often creates a personal or emotional tone, whereas formal language can suggest a more serious, distant tone. Links between words can also help you work it out, e.g., lots of words with connotations of sorrow create a sad tone.

Exercise A — The Shadow of the Wind

Extract from the beginning of Chapter 1

This book was written by Carlos Ruiz Zafón and published in 2001. It is set in Barcelona, Spain in the years following the Spanish Civil War (1936-1939). In this extract, Daniel, the narrator, remembers the day of his first visit to the Cemetery of Forgotten Books, when he was 10 years old. The Cemetery is a huge secret library filled with books that can't be found anywhere else.

I still remember the day my father took me to the Cemetery of Forgotten Books for the first time. It was the early summer of 1945, and we walked through the streets of a Barcelona trapped beneath ashen skies as dawn poured over Rambla de Santa Mónica* in a wreath of liquid copper.

'Daniel, you mustn't tell anyone what you're about to see today,' my father warned. 'Not even your friend Tomás. No one.'

'Not even Mummy?'

My father sighed, hiding behind the sad smile that followed him like a shadow all through his life.

'Of course you can tell her,' he answered, heavy-hearted. 'We keep no secrets from her. You can tell her everything.'

Shortly after the Civil War, an outbreak of cholera* had taken my mother away. We buried her in Montjuïc* on my fourth birthday. The only thing I can recall is that it rained all day and all night, and that when I asked my father whether heaven was crying, he couldn't bring himself to reply. Six years later my mother's absence remained in the air around us, a deafening silence that I had not yet learned to stifle with words. My father and I lived in a modest apartment on Calle Santa Ana, a stone's throw from the church square. The apartment was directly above the bookshop, a legacy from my grandfather, that specialized in rare collectors' editions and secondhand books – an enchanted bazaar*, which my father hoped would one day be mine. I was raised among books, making invisible friends in pages that seemed cast from dust and whose smell I carry on my hands to this day. As a child I learned to fall asleep talking to my mother in the darkness of my bedroom, telling her about the day's events, my adventures at school, and the things I had been taught. I couldn't hear her voice or feel her touch, but her radiance and her warmth haunted every corner of our home, and I believed, with the innocence of those who can still count their age on their ten fingers, that if I closed my eyes and spoke to her, she would be able to hear me wherever she was. Sometimes my father would listen to me from the dining room, crying in silence.

On that June morning, I woke up screaming at first light. My heart was pounding in my chest as if my very soul was trying to escape. My father hurried into my room and held me in his arms, trying to calm me.

'I can't remember her face. I can't remember Mummy's face,' I muttered, breathless.

My father held me tight.

'Don't worry, Daniel. I'll remember for both of us.'

We looked at each other in the half-light, searching for words that didn't exist. For the first time, I realized my father was growing old. He stood up and drew the curtains to let in the pale glint of dawn.

'Come, Daniel, get dressed. I want to show you something,' he said.

Glossary:
Rambla de Santa Mónica — one of the main streets in Barcelona
cholera — an infectious disease caused by dirty, untreated water
Montjuïc — a cemetery in Barcelona
bazaar — a marketplace, especially in the Middle East

Q1 How does the writer try to draw the reader's interest in the first sentence of the extract?

....

....

....

....

Q2 In this extract, the writer uses language to do with light and dark.

a) Write down two examples of light and / or dark language from the text.

1. ....

2. ....

b) Explain the effect of each of the examples you have chosen.

1. ....

....

....

....

2. ....

....

....

....

Q3 Think about the presentation of books in this extract. How has language been used to present them in a mysterious and exciting way?

....

....

....

....

....

....

Q4 This extract has a non-linear structure. What effect does this structure have?

....

....

....

....

....

....

Q5 The narrator of the extract is an adult looking back at childhood memories. Why do you think the writer has chosen to use an adult narrator? Do you think the text would be different if the narrator was still a child? Explain your answer.

....

....

....

....

....

....

Q6 After reading this extract, a student says: "The writer shows how important family love can be." To what extent do you agree with this? Use evidence from the text in your answer.

....

....

....

....

....

....

....

....

Q7 The writer creates a clear sense of grief and loss in this extract.
How does the language in the text contribute to this?

You might want to think about:

- the vocabulary the writer chooses
- how the writer uses figurative language, e.g. similies, metaphors and personification
- any other literary techniques the writer uses.

Sentences come in all shapes and sizes...

Writers will use certain sentences to create specific effects. Short sentences can often help to build tension, while complex sentences can create more detailed descriptions. There are also different sentence types to consider — questions can show a character is confused, while exclamations may indicate excitement.

Exercise B — The Kite Runner

Extract from the opening of the novel

This novel was written by Khaled Hosseini and published in 2003. It is mainly set in 20th-century Afghanistan, although this extract begins in California, USA. In this extract, Amir, the book's narrator, remembers his childhood friend Hassan. As children they shared a love of flying kites.

One day last summer, my friend Rahim Khan called from Pakistan. He asked me to come see him. Standing in the kitchen with the receiver to my ear, I knew it wasn't just Rahim Khan on the line. It was my past of unatoned sins. After I hung up, I went for a walk along Spreckels Lake on the northern edge of Golden Gate Park*. The early-afternoon sun sparkled on the water where dozens of miniature boats sailed, propelled by a crisp breeze. Then I glanced up and saw a pair of kites, red with long blue tails, soaring in the sky. They danced high above the trees on the west end of the park, over the windmills, floating side by side like a pair of eyes looking down on San Francisco, the city I now call home. And suddenly Hassan's voice whispered in my head: *For you, a thousand times over*. Hassan the harelipped* kite runner.

I sat on a park bench near a willow tree. I thought about something Rahim Khan said just before he hung up, almost as an afterthought. *There is a way to be good again*. I looked up at those twin kites. I thought about Hassan. Thought about Baba. Ali. Kabul*. I thought of the life I had lived until the winter of 1975 came and changed everything. And made me what I am today.

When we were children, Hassan and I used to climb the poplar trees in the driveway of my father's house and annoy our neighbours by reflecting sunlight into their homes with a shard of mirror. We would sit across from each other on a pair of high branches, our naked feet dangling, our trouser pockets filled with dried mulberries and walnuts. We took turns with the mirror as we ate mulberries, pelted each other with them, giggling, laughing. I can still see Hassan up on that tree, sunlight flickering through the leaves on his almost perfectly round face, a face like a Chinese doll chiseled from hardwood: his flat, broad nose and slanting, narrow eyes like bamboo leaves, eyes that looked, depending on the light, gold, green, even sapphire. I can still see his tiny low-set ears and that pointed stub of a chin, a meaty appendage that looked like it was added as a mere afterthought. And the cleft lip*, just left of midline, where the Chinese doll maker's instrument may have slipped, or perhaps he had simply grown tired and careless.

Sometimes, up in those trees, I talked Hassan into firing walnuts with his slingshot at the neighbour's one-eyed German shepherd. Hassan never wanted to, but if I asked, *really* asked, he wouldn't deny me. Hassan never denied me anything. And he was deadly with his slingshot. Hassan's father, Ali, used to catch us and get mad, or as mad as someone as gentle as Ali could ever get. He would wag his finger and wave us down from the tree. He would take the mirror and tell us what his mother had told him, that the devil shone mirrors too, shone them to distract Muslims during prayer. "And he laughs while he does it," he always added, scowling at his son.

"Yes, Father," Hassan would mumble, looking down at his feet. But he never told on me. Never told that the mirror, like shooting walnuts at the neighbor's dog, was always my idea.

The poplar trees lined the redbrick driveway, which led to a pair of wrought-iron gates. They in turn opened into an extension of the driveway into my father's estate. The house sat on the left side of the brick path, the backyard at the end of it.

Everyone agreed that my father, my Baba, had built the most beautiful house in the Wazir Akbar Khan district, a new and affluent neighborhood in the northern part of Kabul. Some thought it was the prettiest house in all of Kabul. A broad entryway flanked by rosebushes led to the sprawling house of marble floors and wide windows. Intricate mosaic tiles, handpicked by Baba in Isfahan, covered the floors of the four bathrooms. Gold-stitched tapestries, which Baba had bought in Calcutta, lined the walls; a crystal chandelier hung from the vaulted ceiling.

Glossary:
Golden Gate Park — a park in San Francisco, California
harelipped/cleft lip — a split in the upper lip as a result of it not joining together properly before birth.
Kabul — the capital of Afghanistan

Q1 In the first paragraph of the extract, Amir describes receiving a phone call and then going for a walk. Write down four things we learn about Amir in this paragraph.

1. ....

2. ....

3. ....

4. ....

Kite fighting is a popular sport in Afghanistan, where competitors aim to cut their opponents' kite strings with their own and collect the fallen kites. Later in the novel, we find out that Amir and Hassan used to compete as a team in kite fighting competitions. Amir was in charge of flying the kite while Hassan was his kite runner — the person who captures cut kites.

Q2 Why do you think Hosseini uses an image of two kites on lines 5-7?

....

....

....

....

....

....

Q3 How does Hosseini use structure to set up the story in this extract?

....

....

....

....

....

....

....

Q4 Hosseini uses a lot of descriptive language to describe Hassan in this extract.

a) On line 19, Hassan is described as being like a "doll". Why do you think Hosseini uses this image?

b) How else does Hosseini use language to describe Hassan?
What effect does this language have on the reader's impression of Hassan?

Q5 How does Hosseini present the relationship between Amir and Hassan?
Use evidence from the extract in your answer.

Q6 A student who has read this extract comments, "From line 14 to the end of the extract, the writer brings Amir's childhood in Afghanistan to life for the reader. It's easy to imagine Amir's life and experiences." How far do you agree with this?

You might want to think about:

- your impressions of Amir's childhood
- the techniques the writer uses to present Amir's childhood
- how effective the writer's presentation of Amir's childhood is.

Extension Activity

Characters in novels need to be described effectively to make them believable. The description of Hassan in this extract is a good example of this — it uses language in an interesting way to create a vivid image in the reader's mind. Try writing your own description of someone — it could be a person you know, such as a family member or a friend. Focus on using descriptive language as creatively as you can. No jokes about how big your dad's ears are though.

Exercise C — The Garden of Evening Mists

Extract from Chapter 1

This story by Tan Twan Eng follows a judge living in Kuala Lumpur, Malaysia. In this extract, set in the 1980s, she returns to visit a garden in the Cameron Highlands (a district in Malaysia).

The high wall protecting the garden was patched in moss and old water stains. Ferns grew from the cracks. Set into the wall was a door. Nailed by the doorpost was a wooden plaque, a pair of Japanese ideograms* burned into it. Below these words was the garden's name in English: *Evening Mists*. I felt I was about to enter a place that existed only in the overlapping of air and water, light and time.

Looking above the top of the wall, my eyes followed the uneven treeline of the ridge rising behind the garden. I found the wooden viewing tower half hidden in the trees, like the crow's nest of a galleon that had foundered* among the branches, trapped by a tide of leaves. A path threaded up into the mountains and for a few moments I stared at it, as if I might glimpse Aritomo walking home. Shaking my head, I pushed the door open, entered the garden and closed it behind me.

The sounds of the world outside faded away, absorbed into the leaves. I stood there, not moving. For a moment I felt that nothing had changed since I was last here, almost thirty-five years before — the scent of pine resin sticking to the air, the bamboo creaking and knocking in the breeze, the broken mosaic of sunlight scattered over the ground.

Guided by memory's compass, I began to walk into the garden. I made one or two wrong turns, but came eventually to the pond. I stopped, the twisting walk through the tunnel of trees heightening the effect of seeing the open sky over the water.

Six tall, narrow stones huddled into a miniature limestone mountain range in the centre of the pond. On the opposite bank stood the pavilion, duplicated in the water so that it appeared like a paper lantern hanging in mid-air. A willow grew a few feet away from the pavilion's side, its branches sipping from the pond.

In the shallows, a grey heron cocked its head at me, one leg poised in the air, like the hand of a pianist who had forgotten the notes to his music. It dropped its leg a second later and speared its beak into the water. Was it a descendent of the one that had made its home here when I first came to Yugiri? Frederik had told me that there was always one in the garden — an unbroken chain of solitary birds. I knew it could not be the same bird from nearly forty years before but, as I watched it, I hoped that it was; I wanted to believe that by entering this sanctuary the heron had somehow managed to slip through the fingers of time.

To my right and at the top of an incline stood Aritomo's house. Lights shone from the windows, the kitchen chimney scribbling smoke over the treetops. A man appeared at the front door and walked down the slope towards me. He stopped a few paces away, perhaps to create a space for us to study one another. We are like every single plant and stone and view in the garden, I thought, the distance between one another carefully measured.

'I thought you'd changed your mind,' he said, closing the space between us.

'The drive was longer than I remembered.'

'Places seem further apart, don't they, the older we get.'

At sixty seven years old, Frederik Pretorius had the dignified air given off by an antique art work, secure in the knowledge of its own rarity and value. We had kept in touch over the years, meeting up for drinks or a meal whenever he came down to Kuala Lumpur, but I had always resisted his invitations to visit Cameron Highlands. In the last two or three years his trips to KL had tapered off. Long ago I had realised he was the only close friend I would ever have.

'The way you were watching that bird just now,' he said, 'I felt you were looking back to the past.'

I turned to look at the heron again. The bird had moved further out into the pond. Mist escaped from the water's surface, whispers only the wind could catch. 'I was thinking of the old days.'

Glossary:
ideograms — written characters
foundered — sunk

Q1 In the first two paragraphs, the narrator describes the wall surrounding the garden and what she can see above it.

Write down four things we learn about the wall from these descriptions.

1. ....

2. ....

3. ....

4. ....

In 'The Garden of Evening Mists', the narrator's sister dreams of making her own traditional Japanese garden. When her sister dies, the narrator decides to build a Japanese garden in her memory. To learn the necessary skills, the narrator becomes the apprentice of a famous Japanese garden designer, Aritomo, who at that time was building the garden described in the extract.

Q2 Look back at lines 10-20. How has the writer used language to describe the garden in these lines? Pick out three techniques the writer uses, give examples and explain their effect.

Technique: ....

Example: ....

Effect: ....

....

....

Technique: ....

Example: ....

Effect: ....

....

....

Technique: ....

Example: ....

Effect: ....

....

....

Frederik Pretorius is the nephew of Magnus Pretorius, a friend the narrator went to visit after World War Two. Magnus owned a tea plantation which Frederik worked on and later inherited. It was during the narrator's visit to Magnus that she met Aritomo, whose garden was near Magnus's tea plantation.

Q3 In the extract, the narrator meets with Frederik Pretorius. How does the writer present their relationship? Use evidence from the extract in your answer.

....

....

....

....

....

....

....

....

....

....

....

Q4 Think about the structure of this extract. How does the writer make it interesting for the reader?

....

....

....

....

....

....

....

....

....

....

Q5 One student who read this extract said, "The writer makes the reader feel sympathy for the narrator. She is clearly nostalgic about the garden and seems to wish she could go back in time." How far do you agree with this?

You might want to think about:

- how the writer creates a sense of nostalgia
- whether this increases the reader's sympathy
- how language and structure contributes to these things.

Get your finest pen at the ready...

Annotating an extract can help you get to grips with it by allowing you to pick out important features more easily. There are lots of ways to annotate a text, such as underlining and highlighting. Only scribble on a text if you're allowed to though — you don't want to go ruining any of your teacher's prized first editions...

Answers

Section One — Secrets and Lies

Pages 2-4: Exercise A — 'Mr Norris Changes Trains'

1. a) Any four things about Mr Norris's appearance, either directly quoted or paraphrased, from lines 1-6. Answers may include:
   - He has manicured hands.
   - His face is less rosy than usual.
   - There are rings under his eyes.
   - He wears a wig.

   b) You might have said that Mr Norris seems stressed because the "rings under his eyes" suggest he hasn't slept recently. You could have also said that he cares about his appearance, shown by his "manicured hands" and the fact he wears a wig.

It's fine if you gave a different impression of Mr Norris — just make sure that you've linked your answer back to the text.

2. You should have explained how the language used to describe each character increases the tension in this part of the extract. Here are some things you could have mentioned:
   - Mr Norris stops suddenly "as if he'd been shot." This simile creates tension by making the reader think about violence, which makes the situation feel more fraught with danger.
   - Mr Norris exclaims "Oh dear!" twice. This repetition emphasises his fear, creating tension by making the reader curious about what could make him so afraid.
   - The intruder is described as having a "strange, loud, angry voice". This list of three adjectives emphasises the danger the intruder poses, which increases tension because it makes the reader worried about what he might do.
   - The intruder often speaks in short, exclamatory sentences: "I tell you he's here!" This angry tone increases the tension by implying he is determined and violent.
3. You could have said that it conveys two different atmospheres — the threatening atmosphere outside the flat and the fearful atmosphere inside. These contrasting atmospheres create tension by both showing that Mr Norris is scared and repeatedly reminding the reader of the reason for his fear.
4. Any two sounds from these lines and their effect. Here are some things you could have mentioned:
   - "click" — The onomatopoeic use of sound draws attention to the fact that the door is locked, emphasising that the characters are now trapped inside.
   - "thud" — This onomatopoeic word suggests the "young man" was thrown forcefully and that the intruder is strong.
   - "rattling" — This makes the locked door sound rickety and easily breakable, creating suspense as the reader worries that the intruder will break through.
5. You should have given your opinion on the statement and explained your ideas using evidence from the text.
   If you agreed with the statement, you could have mentioned:
   - Mr Norris doesn't tell the narrator what is going on, which leaves the reader to wonder why the intruder has arrived. This makes the reader want to keep reading to find out more about the intruder, but it also creates tension, as the reader does not know how much danger Mr Norris is in.
   - As the narrator is inside the flat, he is only able to give a small amount of information about what's happening outside the flat to the reader. This keeps the reader engaged by encouraging them to fill in the details of who the intruder might be and what is happening outside the flat.

   If you disagreed with the statement, you could have mentioned:
   - While the narrative viewpoint is important, other factors, such as the changing focus, play a larger role in keeping the reader interested. Repeatedly shifting between the events inside and outside of the flat reminds the reader of the threat that the intruder might get in. This makes the reader want to keep reading to find out if the intruder manages to get inside.

Pages 5-7: Exercise B — 'The Thirteenth Tale'

1. a) You should have described Winter's attitude to truth in the first two paragraphs. Here are some things you could have said:
   - She thinks that people who love truth are boring.
   - She is annoyed by truth being linked to storytelling.
   - She thinks that truth is useless compared to a story.

   b) You should have said that language is used to give a negative impression of truth. Truth is described as "hard-boned and fleshless". These adjectives make truth sound unyielding or even skeleton-like, which carries connotations of fear.

   c) You should have said that language is used to describe lies as comforting. Winter describes lies as having a "soothing, rocking safety". This evokes the image of a baby in a crib being rocked to sleep, which creates a sense of contentment.

Don't worry if you have described different effects in b) and c) — just make sure that you've explained how language is used to create these effects.

2. a) You should have explained what the third and fourth paragraphs tell you about Winter's attitude towards reporters, using examples to explain your answer. Here are some things you could have mentioned:
   - She refers to reporters as "hacks", often used as a derogatory term, which suggests she thinks they are bad at their jobs.
   - The description of the reporters as trying to "catch" her "out" suggests she thinks they are devious.
   - She thinks reporters are easily manipulated. Her fake stories are "bait" to them, showing they can be enticed like prey.

   b) You should have talked about the effect of structure in the third, fourth and fifth paragraphs and explained your answer. Here are some things you could have mentioned:
   - The non-linear structure shows that Winter has lied to reporters for a long time. First, she implies that she currently lies in interviews instead of giving the "same old answers". Then she goes back in time to describe how she made up stories to reporters in the "early years" and continued to do so after she "became famous". This emphasises how Winter has repeatedly lied in the past right through to the present.
   - The third paragraph sets up a contrast between reporters as "hacks" and writers who are "the real thing." This makes the reader view them as being in opposition for the next few paragraphs, with each trying to gain the upper hand.
3. You should have talked about how language is used in the given quote to suggest that Winter is a confident character. Here are some things you could have mentioned:
   - Winter's reference to her "genius" is blunt and straightforward. This shows that she has no doubts about her intelligence and emphasises her self-confidence.
   - The use of the possessive "my" creates a proud tone and hints that she sees her "genius" as superior to other people's.

Don't worry if you talked about different language features — just make sure that you explained how they suggest Winter is a confident character.

4. You should have talked about how language is used to suggest that Winter is an effective liar, using examples to explain your answer. Here are some things you could have mentioned:
   - The writer makes journalists sound easily led by Winter's lies. She describes Winter's fake stories as "bait to draw them gently" away from their aims during interviews. The use of "bait" makes journalists sound like animals being lured. This suggests they are less intelligent than Winter, and implies that she can control them with her lies.
   - The writer makes the journalists sound captivated by Winter's lies. They had a "dreamy" look during interviews with her, which suggests a pleasant detachment from reality. This shows how effectively Winter is able to mesmerise them with her lies.
   - The writer uses a semantic field of words associated with sewing such as "woven", "stitching" and "sequins". This creates an image of Winter fabricating stories in a way that requires skill, reflecting her ability to craft effective lies.

Answers

Pages 8-11: Exercise C — 'The Adventure of the Priory School'

1. You should have talked about what Holmes's language in line 2 suggests about his character, using examples to support your view. Here are some things you could have mentioned:
   - Holmes comes across as polite and respectful. He addresses the Duke as "your Grace", which implies that he respects the Duke's higher social status.
   - Holmes is well-spoken. He uses language such as "confess", "beg" and "explicit", which sounds more sophisticated than, for example, 'admit', 'ask' and 'clear'. This articulate language suggests that Holmes is well-educated.
   - Holmes seems purposeful. He encourages the Duke to give a detailed account of what happened, urging him to "be more explicit". This imperative sentence creates a firm tone, which shows how Holmes is determined to get to the truth.
2. You should have said that the Duke fell in love with a woman who refused to marry him for fear that she'd affect his career. After she died, the Duke raised her son, James, but didn't acknowledge him as his son. James worked out that the Duke was his father and blackmailed him. He also hated the Duke's legitimate son, Arthur. Despite this, the Duke cared for James for his mother's sake.
3. After kidnapping Arthur, James planned to give him back to the Duke in return for becoming the sole heir in the Duke's will.
4. You should have said if you think the reader is meant to feel sympathy for James, using examples to explain your answer. If you felt the reader is supposed to feel sympathy for James, you could have mentioned:
   - James seems to be sidelined by his father. The Duke wouldn't "acknowledge" that he was James's father because the resulting scandal would have been "abhorrent" to him. This shows that the Duke did what was best for himself rather than for James. By making James seem unfairly treated, the reader is encouraged to feel sympathy for him.
   - James seems upset by the outcomes of his actions. He was "overwhelmed with grief" and "seized with horror" by the news of Heidegger's death. The verbs "overwhelmed" and "seized" emphasise how he can't escape his feelings of remorse, allowing the reader to sympathise with him.

   If you felt the reader isn't supposed to feel any sympathy for James, you could have mentioned:
   - James is described in unpleasant terms — for example, he acts with "persistent hatred" toward Arthur, who is only a child. The use of "persistent" makes his hostility sound unending. This portrays James as relentlessly cruel, making it hard to sympathise with him.
   - James acts in criminal ways to get what he wants. He kidnaps Arthur in a "wicked scheme" which results in Heidegger's death. Although James is "overwhelmed with grief" by this death, it's impossible to sympathise with him because his plan caused it to happen.
5. a) You could have said it means that the Duke was worried that James would harm Arthur.
   b) You could have said it means that James's evil plans were ruined when Heidegger's body was found.
   c) You could have said it means that the Duke accused James of killing Heidegger.
6. You should have said how the extract has been structured to keep you interested. Here are some things you could have mentioned:
   - The first line ("It was Holmes's turn to look astonished.") grabs the reader's attention. The adjective "astonished" shows his surprise, and implies that what is about to follow will be exciting. Using this right before the Duke reveals his story makes the reader eager to read on.
   - The Duke's story is structured chronologically — it first reveals James's motivations, then his plan to kidnap Arthur, and finally Heidegger's death and Arthur's discovery. This structure involves the reader in the story by giving a complete explanation. It also creates tension as the reader is left waiting to find out if Arthur is safe.
7. a) You should have talked about the effect of having so much speech from the Duke in the extract. Here are some things you could have mentioned:
   - The Duke dominates the conversation without any interruptions from Holmes. This suggests that Holmes is listening intently to his story.
   - So much speech from the Duke allows the reader to immerse themselves in the story that he is telling. His long speech gives an overview of events which engages the reader by giving them a clear picture of what happened.

   b) You should have given your overall impression of the Duke. Here are some things you could have mentioned:
   - The Duke seems like an honourable man because he said that he "would certainly never have" married anyone else if James's mother had lived, and he continues to look after James despite his attempts at blackmail.
   - The Duke seems selfish, as he seems to care more about his social standing than about James. He denies James a father in order to be seen as abiding by social norms and is scared of James revealing the truth and ruining his reputation, which was particular important at the time.

Don't worry if you have a different impression of the Duke — just make sure that you've explained why you have this impression of him.

Section Two — New Places

Pages 12-15: Exercise A — 'The Miniaturist'

1. a) Any four things about Nella's surroundings, either directly quoted or paraphrased, from the correct part of the extract. Answers might include:
   - It is warm.
   - There is a canal.
   - The houses are grand.
   - The clouds are orange.

   b) You might have said that the author makes Amsterdam sound like a place you would like to live in because the houses are described as being very "beautiful". This suggests the quality of life for people in those houses is good.
2. The technique used is a rhetorical question. You could have talked about how it emphasises Nella's uncertainty by showing that she is questioning her own memory.

Don't worry if you've mentioned a different effect from the one above — just make sure that you've used evidence from the text to support your view.

3. You can give any opinion as long as you explain it using examples from the extract. You might have mentioned that:
   - Nella does seem young and childlike in this extract. She remembers what her mother has told her in the past, which suggests that her mother's advice still has a direct influence on her life. She also slaps her shoes down on the floor to try to get someone's attention, which isn't what an adult would usually do — an adult might call out again or walk inside the house, so this makes Nella seem quite childish.
   - Nella might be young, but she handles the situation she has found herself in maturely. She removes her shoes to "show that country girls have manners too", suggesting she is aware that she needs to give the right impression. This awareness makes her seem grown-up, as adults tend to be more socially aware than children.
4. You should have written about the effects of writing in the present tense. Here are some things you could have said:
   - The present tense makes it seem like the action happens as the reader is reading the story, which is exciting.
   - The present tense increases suspense because there are no hints of what is going to happen next.

Answers

5. You should have written about what the descriptions of hair could suggest about the characters. Here are some things you could have mentioned:
   - Nella's hair is "loosened", which could symbolise her lack of control over her situation as well as reminding the reader that Nella has travelled a long way to be there.
   - The description of Marin's hair makes her sound very tidy. The fact that "Not a wisp" escapes suggests she is a perfectionist and cares about portraying herself as such.
   - The contrast between each character's hair sets them up as opposites. Whereas Nella's hair lets "wisps escape", Marin's lets "Not a wisp" escape. This hints that they have different personalities and may not get along.
6. You should have talked about how the eerie tone has been created. Here are some things you could have mentioned:
   - Nella describes the inside of the house as a "void" as she peers in through the door. This creates an eerie tone and suggests that the house is dark and mysterious inside.
   - Personification is used to say the canal seems to "hold its breath". This creates an eerie tone by adding suspense as people hold their breath when waiting nervously.
   - The woman who speaks to Nella "glides from the shadows", which makes her seem almost ghostlike. The unnatural image creates an eerie tone as it suggests to the reader that something isn't right.
   - The dialogue in line 28 interrupts the flow of Nella's thoughts. Before it, the reader is distracted by Nella observing a woman outside, and worrying about her hair, so the woman's question is unexpected and a little startling. This sudden disruption makes the reader feel wary about the house and its occupants, adding to the sense of eeriness around them.
   - The author reveals the identity of the woman in the shadow after she has spoken, so neither Nella nor the reader knows who it is when they hear the voice. The gender of the voice also isn't revealed when they speak, adding to the mystery of who the voice belongs to. This heightens the eerie tone by portraying the woman as mysterious.

7. a) You should have given an example of sensory language from the text. Answers might include:
   - "rare October warmth"
   - "cool air rises from the marble"
   - "she calls - loud, a little panicked"
   - "thrills the tips of his feathers against the cage bars"
   - "she slaps the shoes down"
   - "light breeze letting wisps escape"
   - "tickling her face"
   - "Nella's skin contracts"
   - "can't banish the goosebumps"

   b) You should have explained the effect of the sensory language the author uses. Here are some things you could have mentioned:
   - The author uses language related to the sense of touch to help convey the setting. Descriptions such as "October warmth", "cool air" and "light breeze" help the reader to feel as if they are in Amsterdam with Nella.
   - The feeling of touch helps the reader understand Nella's emotions. The reader is told that her "skin contracts" and that she has "goosebumps." These physical descriptions show the reader that Nella is feeling afraid after discovering that she was being watched.
   - The use of sound helps to show Nella's unease. She "calls" out into the house, a sound which is described as "loud, a little panicked." This sound conveys to the reader her anxiety at no-one coming to the door to greet her.

8. You should have given your opinion on the statement and explained your ideas using evidence from the text.
   If you agreed with the statement, you could have mentioned:
   - There is a hint of unpleasantness to Amsterdam. The part of the canal that Nella is near is known as the "Golden Bend", which makes it sound grand and spectacular, but when Nella sees the canal it is "brown and workaday", which makes it seem dirty and dull. The difference between the name and the reality is unsettling, which helps the reader understand why Nella might feel uncomfortable.
   - The woman that Nella meets in the house seems strange and unwelcoming, which would understandably make Nella feel uncomfortable. The woman approaches Nella without saying anything and has a "solemn" expression. This creates a sense of uneasiness, as the reader might have expected her to be more friendly towards Nella, who is a guest.
   - Nella is presented as being out of her depth in Amsterdam. She is a "country" girl who wants to prove that she has "manners too", which suggests that she feels social pressures in the city. The fact that she "feels a fool" after her attempts to get someone's attention in the house suggests that she isn't handling the situation very well, which helps the reader understand why she feels so uncomfortable.

You could have disagreed or only partially agreed with the statement — as long as you use evidence to back up your opinion.

Pages 16-19: Exercise B — 'The Enchanted April'

1. You should have said that the room described in lines 4-5 doesn't sound appealing. You might have mentioned the "bare white walls", the "stone floor" and beds "made of iron" which make the room sound empty, uncomfortable and cold.

However, you could have mentioned that the "bright flowers" give the room a hint of colour, interest and homeliness.

2. You should have said that the writer uses hyperbole. This uses exaggeration in order to emphasise how Mrs. Wilkins feels like it has been a long time since she was last in Hampstead.
3. a) You could have said that lines 15-19 show that Mrs. Wilkins is happy with her room. She describes it as "delicious", which uses synaesthesia to highlight her enjoyment. You could have also said that the repetition of "her room" and "her own" shows that she enjoys having ownership over the room.

   b) You should have talked about the effect of the quotes and what they might suggest about Mrs. Wilkins's character. Here are some things you could have mentioned:
   - The word "sweet" implies that the room is pleasant, but "like a cell" suggests it is uncomfortable. This hints that Mrs. Wilkins is trying to convince herself that she likes the room.
   - The use of "like a cell" suggests that the room is basic, but "sweet" suggests that this pleases Mrs. Wilkins. This suggests that Mrs. Wilkins prefers plainness to flashy decor.

4. a) You could have said that the writer chose to use a single word of speech to show that Mrs Wilkins is overwhelmed by what she sees out of her window. This creates a sense of anticipation in the reader because it makes you want to know what's out there. Or, you could have said that using this single word and not giving any further information until the next paragraph builds suspense.

   b) You should have given one other way the extract is structured to show Mrs. Wilkins's enjoyment of her surroundings. Here are some things you could have mentioned:
   - The first paragraph questions "What would she see out of her window?", making it seem like the view from the window will be the main focus of the extract. However, this question isn't answered until line 26. This reflects how Mrs. Wilkins is taking her time to enjoy her surroundings inside before looking outside.
   - The two paragraphs after Mrs. Wilkins opens the shutters are split into describing the view and her thoughts on its beauty. Dedicating most of a lengthy paragraph to her reaction, longer than the paragraph describing the view, reflects how much she enjoys the view.

5. a) Personification.

   b) You should have said that the use of personification makes the sea and mountains feel alive. You could have also said that

Answers

describing them as "asleep" makes the scenery seem calm.

c) You should have explained how else language is used to describe Mrs. Wilkins's surroundings in lines 25-33 and its effect on the reader. Here are some things you could have said:
   - The writer uses repetition, repeating the phrases "Such beauty" and "How beautiful". This reinforces the beauty of Mrs. Wilkins's surroundings to the reader.
   - A simile is used to describe the peacefulness of Mrs. Wilkins's surroundings. The "motionless fishing boats" are compared to "a flock of white birds". This simile makes the reader picture the boats as a natural part of the scenery and reminds the reader of doves, which often symbolise peace.
   - The writer describes the cypress tree as "a great black sword" cutting through the "delicate" colours of the mountains and the sea. This makes the reader picture the tree as a powerful weapon, contrasting the "delicate" colours which create a sense of peace. This makes the cypress tree stand out as a key feature of the landscape in the reader's mind.

6. You should have said what impression you get of Mrs. Wilkins's feelings towards Mellersh and how the writer creates this. Here are some things you could have mentioned:
   - Mrs. Wilkins finds life with Mellersh restrictive. She describes "the freedom of one's movements" in bed on her own compared to in the bed she shares with Mellersh. This hints that Mrs. Wilkins doesn't feel free with Mellersh.
   - Mrs. Wilkins finds Mellersh unpleasant. She imagines him "angry" in the "dim mugginess" of England, suggesting that she associates him with unpleasant feelings.

7. You should have said how the writer suggests that Mrs. Wilkins is happier in Italy than in England and given examples from the text. Here are some things you could have mentioned:
   - The writer uses adjectives to show that Mrs. Wilkins is happier in Italy. She repeats words like "delicious", "beautiful" and "happy" to describe Italy and how it makes her feel. The repetition of positive adjectives creates an upbeat tone that reflects Mrs. Wilkins's happiness in Italy.
   - The description of the two locations makes Mrs. Wilkins seem happier in Italy. In Italy, her face is "bathed in light". The use of "bathed" makes the sunlight sound refreshing. However, Hampstead is described as having a "dim mugginess", making it sound uncomfortable. This contrast makes it seem like Mrs. Wilkins is more comfortable in Italy than in England.
   - The writer uses a list to show Mrs. Wilkins dislikes living in England. She lists aspects of the discomfort she feels when living there: "aches, hurts, discouragements". This list emphasises her suffering while in England and contrasts with the positive experience she is having in Italy.

Pages 20-23: Exercise C — 'Life of Pi'

1. You should have explored how the writer engages the reader's attention in the first paragraph and explained your answer. Here are some things you could have mentioned:
   - The writer draws the reader in with the opening sentence "I made an exceptional botanical discovery." The adjective "exceptional" suggests that what follows will be exciting. This makes the reader want to read on to find out more.
   - The writer states that there will be "many who disbelieve the following episode". This creates the impression that something unusual or exciting is going to happen, which entices the reader to keep reading.

2. Any four things about the island, either quoted or paraphrased, from the correct part of the extract. Answers might include:
   - It is low-lying.
   - It has no soil.
   - It has trees.
   - It is filled with a "dense mass of vegetation".

3. a) You should have written that this simile shows Pi's disbelief at what he is seeing. Comparing his eyelids to "lumberjacks" shows that he expects the trees to be 'chopped down' when he closes his eyes and the island to be gone when he opens them. This suggests that Pi believes the island is not real.

   b) You should have talked about whether you think Pi's descriptions of the island make it sound unusual and given examples from the text to support your answer. Here are some things you could have mentioned:
   - Pi makes the island seem unusual by presenting his thoughts. Pi's description of the trees as "like none I had ever seen before" emphasises that the island appears very strange, helping the reader to understand how odd it looks.
   - Pi makes the island sound unusual through his description of the trees. Pi describes the trees on the island as having "equally distributed branches" with "emerald" leaves. These descriptions present the trees as unbelievably perfect and beautiful, which arouses the reader's suspicion that the island is somewhat unusual or even fantastical.

Don't worry if you didn't think the writer's descriptions of the island make it sound unusual — just make sure that you've used evidence from the text to support your view.

4. You should have talked about how the writer uses colour to describe the island in lines 20-26 and used evidence from the text. Here are some things you could have mentioned:
   - The writer's repetition of colour shows what the island looks like. "Green" is repeated six times in these lines, which makes the greenness of the island seem overwhelming.
   - The writer describes the island's green colour as outshining "food colouring and flashing neon lights". This suggests that it is a green that can only be achieved naturally — it's better than anything artificial or man-made.
   - The writer uses the narrator's thoughts about colour to describe the island positively. Pi says that green is "the colour of Islam" and "my favourite colour". These thoughts show a deep fondness for the island's colour, making the island seem comforting.

5. You should have circled 'first person' and explained the effect of this narrative viewpoint. Here are some things you could have mentioned:
   - It allows the reader to see the changing feelings of Pi, such as his "satisfaction" and "disappointment". This makes him easier to relate to.
   - It lets the reader experience discovering the island just as Pi did. The use of a first-person narrative means it's hard for the reader to believe the island is real until Pi confirms it, which he takes a long time to do. This causes the reader to experience the same tension and disbelief as Pi.

6. You should have given your opinion on the statement and explained your ideas using evidence from the text.
   - If you agreed with the statement, you could have said that Pi seems unreliable because of his reluctance to accept that the island is real. For example, Pi says the island is an "illusion" many times in the extract. This suggests that Pi doubted his sanity at the time and makes his account of events seem unreliable.
   - If you disagreed with the statement, you could have said that Pi seems reliable because he acknowledges that his situation is unusual. For example, he asks "Who had ever heard of land with no soil?". This rhetorical question presents him as a logical person with an understanding of the world, making him seem reliable.

7. You could have talked about how the tone changes from sceptical to excited in lines 31-38. For example, Pi initially uses short, definite sentences such as "Still I did not sink. Still I did not believe." to emphasise that while he is putting his weight on the island, he is determined to believe that it isn't real. As Pi starts to believe in the island, longer sentences are introduced to reflect his excitement.

Don't worry if you've talked about something different — just make sure that you've used evidence from the text to support your answer.

Answers

8. You should have written about how the extract is structured to make the text interesting for the reader and the effect this creates. Here are some things you could have mentioned:
   - The structure gives the reader a clear idea of the island by addressing each sense in turn. The writer details how the island looks, describing the trees as "brilliantly green", then how it feels ("rubbery") and finally the "overwhelming" smell. Splitting the sensory language in this way gives the reader time to build an image of the island in their minds and become invested in finding out more about it.
   - The text is structured to make the reader question whether the island is real. The start of the extract makes the reader expect the island to be unusual by saying that people will "disbelieve the following episode". The extract develops by describing the island in unusual ways, making the reader question whether the island is an "illusion", before the end of the extract reveals that the island does exist. Withholding this information until the end creates intrigue, as the reader waits to find out the true nature of the island.
   - The writer structures the extract by starting numerous paragraphs with short sentences. Having these at the beginning of the paragraph slows down the progress of the story, creating tension as the reader waits to find out more about the island and whether it is real.

Section Three — The Supernatural

Pages 24-27: Exercise A — 'The Haunting of Hill House'

1. You should have said how the first paragraph makes you feel and explained why. You could have written that you felt:
   - Afraid. The verb "whispering" highlights the character's fear of being discovered which implies that the unseen force is harmful.
   - Curious. The pronoun "It" and the phrase "as though" are ambiguous, so the reader doesn't know for sure what the presence is or what it wants to do. You could add that this encourages you to read on to find out more.

Don't worry if you've written about a different emotion — just make sure that you've used evidence from the text to back up your answer.

2. You should have talked about how Eleanor is affected by the supernatural force in the third paragraph, giving examples to support your points. Here are some things you could have mentioned:
   - Eleanor hears a loud noise which she believes is inside her head. She says she will "never be able to sleep again" because of the noise "inside my head". This emphasises her distress and suggests that the unseen force is inside her.
   - She feels like she is going mad. She says she is "disappearing inch by inch" and "going apart a little bit at a time". This suggests that the supernatural force is affecting her mental health and that she is struggling to cope.
3. a) You should have talked about how language is used to describe the sound in lines 11-13, using examples to explain its effect. Here are some things you could have mentioned:
   - The adjective "overwhelming" gives the impression that the noise was uncomfortably loud and unavoidable. The simile "washed over her like waves" reinforces this idea by comparing the sound to an unstoppable force of nature.
   - The adjective "metallic" creates an image of metal in the reader's mind. Metal is hard and unyielding, which suggests that the noise is forceful and persistent.

   b) You should have talked about how language is used to describe the sounds in lines 19-24, using examples to explain its effect. Here are some things you could have mentioned:
   - The noise in the corridor sounds like "an animal pacing back and forth". This comparison to an animal emphasises how wild and aggressive the sound seems.
   - Language usually associated with babies and children ("the little babbling murmur" and "the tiny laughter") is used to describe the supernatural force outside the door. This sounds unnerving, emphasising how unsettled Eleanor is.
4. You should have talked about why you think the author uses different narrative viewpoints. You could have said that the third-person perspective allows the author to describe what happens, for example, when "the house shivered". The first-person perspective lets the reader see how these events affect Eleanor, for example, she says that she feels she is "going apart a little bit at a time".
5. You should have talked about the effect of repetition in the extract, using examples to support your points. Here are some things you could have mentioned:
   - It shows the reader how terrified the characters are. For example, Theodora repeats "It can't get in" to herself "over and over". This suggests she can't focus on anything but the immediate danger, highlighting her fear to the reader.
   - It shows that the characters are losing control. Theodora says "purest love" twice for no clear reason. The repetition of this nonsensical phrase shows how fear has caused the characters to act like children instead of their normal selves.
6. You should have talked about how the extract is structured to create a sense of fear in the reader. Here are some things you could have mentioned:
   - Most of the paragraphs are short and move quickly between characters speaking, Eleanor's thoughts and descriptions of the supernatural presence. This makes it seem like things are rapidly getting out of control for the characters, which makes the reader fearful for what might happen to them.
   - The narrative keeps returning to Eleanor's thoughts which are about her fear of the supernatural force. Frequently returning to Eleanor's scared thoughts reinforces how terrified she is, which makes the reader also feel fearful.
   - The final paragraph disrupts the flow of the narrative. After focusing on how the unseen force struggles to get into the room the characters are in for nine paragraphs, the author unexpectedly expands their focus to the house as a whole. This makes the unseen force seem like a larger problem as it violently "shook" the house, causing the pictures to fall down and the glass to break. This creates fear in the reader by showing them what the unseen force is capable of.
7. You should have given your opinion on the statement and explained your ideas using evidence from the text.
   If you agreed with the statement, you could have mentioned:
   - Much of the language which describes Eleanor indicates that she is spiralling into madness, which is what makes the extract scary. The descriptions of Eleanor putting "her hands to her mouth to feel if her face was still there", and questioning herself ("is that me?") emphasise her instability. Eleanor's behaviour illustrates the power of the unknown threat, which creates fear in the reader by showing how much danger the characters are in.
   - The characters' fear is what effectively makes the extract scary. The language used to describe Luke's response to the threat is intense, as he "gestured furiously" and speaks "tensely". The adverbs "furiously" and "tensely" suggest he is agitated and afraid, which carries over to the reader. Luke's mental clarity and rational dialogue emphasises this fear — if even he's afraid, there's clearly something to be afraid of.
   - The language describing the supernatural threat doesn't contribute to the scariness of this extract. The unseen threat is described as having a "little caressing touch" and "tiny laughter". The adjectives "little" and "tiny" make the supernatural threat sound weak and unintimidating.

   If you disagreed with the statement, you could have mentioned:
   - The final paragraph is what makes the extract scary by demonstrating how powerful the unseen threat is. The whole house "shivered and shook" and Theodora is heard to say that the house is "coming down". This suggests that

Answers

everyone in the house is at the mercy of the unseen force, which reflects its power. Delaying the reveal of this power until the end of the extract makes it scarier because it allows the reader to hope that the characters might be safe before suddenly undermining this belief.

You could also have said that the scariness of the extract equally depends on both the characters and the threat itself. To do this, you would need to give examples from the extract of both being scary.

Pages 28-31: Exercise B — 'The Island of Doctor Moreau'

1. You should have ticked boxes c) and e) only.
2. You should have explained what the island is like in your own words. Here are some things you could have mentioned:
   - The island has an unusual shape.
   - It is at a low altitude / is close to the sea.
   - The island was formed by a volcano.
   - It has coral reefs on three sides.
   - Gases are released from fumaroles, and earthquakes occasionally take place.
3. a) You could have said it refers to the two Beast People which Prendick was the most afraid of, because "formidable" can mean 'frightening'. You might also have said it refers to the two most dangerous Animal Men, as "formidable" can also mean 'threatening'.

   b) You should have talked about the effect listing has on the reader. Here are some things you could have mentioned:
   - Listing creates the impression of large numbers, which shows the reader that there are many types of Beast People.
   - Listing makes Prendick sound as if he is surrounded by Beast People, which emphasises that Prendick is outnumbered and possibly in danger.
4. You should have talked about the impression you get of Montgomery and explained why. Here are some things you could have mentioned:
   - Montgomery is a supportive person. He helps Prendick get used to his new surroundings — phrases such as "Montgomery informed me" suggest that Montgomery has been a useful source of information for Prendick. This shows Montgomery helping Prendick adapt to the island.
   - Montgomery is a kind person. He regards the Beast People as "normal human beings", showing he doesn't discriminate them for how they were created. This portrays Montgomery as kind hearted to the Beast People.
   - Montgomery seems to dislike humanity. Montgomery sees humans as "dangerous, and cold-hearted" and has a "vicious sympathy" for the Beast People. This implies that he is isolating himself from mankind and becoming closer to the Beast People.
5. You should have talked about how the extract is structured to reveal information about the Beast People. Here are some things you could have mentioned:
   - They are mentioned in the first line, but the focus of the paragraph shifts to a description of the island. It isn't until the end of the paragraph that the focus shifts back to the Beast People. This builds anticipation and makes the reader want to learn about the mysterious Beast People.
   - The author gradually goes into more detail about the Beast People. In the second paragraph, they are described in terms of their "general appearance", before the third paragraph becomes more specific. Separating the information in this way slowly introduces the reader to aspects of the Beast People, helping them to understand what the Beast People are like.
6. You should have talked about the effect that the lack of detailed descriptions has on the reader. Here are some things you could have mentioned:
   - It gives the Beast People an air of mystery. By never making it clear exactly what they look like, the reader has to imagine the creatures themselves. This encourages the reader to engage with the text.
   - It makes the Beast People seem more frightening. By not giving all the details about them, the Beast People seem like an unknown, dangerous entity. This could make the reader fear the Beast People.
   - Describing the beasts straightforwardly ("Leopard-man") gives the extract a more factual and scientific tone because the focus is on the facts rather than elaborate descriptions. This makes the extract seem more realistic.
7. You should have talked about how Prendick's feelings towards the Beast People change, using examples to support your points. Here are some things you could have mentioned:
   - Prendick initially had a "shivering horror" of the Beast People and regarded them as "brutes". This suggests he was frightened and disgusted by the Beast People. The repetition of "brutes" emphasises the repulsion he felt.
   - Prendick says that he became "habituated" to the Beast People. This suggests that he grew more comfortable with them over time. Prendick also says that he began to see the Beast People as "natural and ordinary", implying that he stopped viewing them as experiments against nature.
   - Although Prendick becomes more comfortable with the Beast People, he still seems suspicious of them. He uses the negative adjectives "shifty" and "cunning" to describe the Fox-bear's face, which suggests that although he is beginning to think of them as more human, he sees negative aspects of humanity in their characters.

Pages 32-35: Exercise C — 'The Haunting of Alaizabel Cray'

1. You should have talked about the impression of London you get from the first paragraph and included quotes to support your views. Here are some things you could have mentioned:
   - London is full of criminal activity at night (such as the reference to "opium dens"), which makes it seem unsafe.
   - London has "dirty streets", which suggests that it is unclean. This makes it seem like an unpleasant place to live.
   - It seems to be a very busy place, full of people from all walks of life such as "tram drivers" and "solicitors". This gives the impression that it is a thriving city.
2. a) You should have given three examples of weather being personified in the second and third paragraphs. Here are some things you could have mentioned:
   - "crawling steadily"
   - "the fury of the rain"
   - "jabbing forked sparks of lightning"
   - "booming with terrible rage"

   b) You should have talked about the effect that personifying the weather has on the reader. Here are some things you could have mentioned:
   - Personification makes the weather seem more threatening. The verb "jabbing" to describe the lightning suggests a painful and angry movement, and the "fury" and "rage" of the storm emphasises the threat it brings to London. This makes the reader aware of how severe a storm it will be.
   - Personification makes the storm appear menacing. The clouds "crawling steadily" suggests that the storm is deliberately and slowly heading to London. This makes it seem as though the storm is aware of the disruption it intends to cause, which makes it appear more threatening.
3. You should have found a simile from the correct part of the text and explained how it affects the reader. Here are some things you could have mentioned:
   - "like water down a plughole"
     This creates a familiar image to help the reader imagine the unusual scene. It highlights that there is a lot of cloud and that this cloud is focused only on London.
   - "settled upon them like ash"
     This has connotations of destruction, because ash is formed during fires and volcanic eruptions. It gives the reader the impression that something bad is about to happen.

Answers

- "Like a slow whirlpool of blood"
  The reference to "blood" makes this a distressing image which leaves the reader feeling uneasy and could foreshadow the result of the wych-kin's attack on London.

4. You should have talked about how the extract is structured to guide the reader through the storm. Here are some things you could have mentioned:
   - Time-markers show how the storm develops. The reader is given updates, for example, at "mid-afternoon", "four o'clock", "six o'clock". These give the reader a clear idea of the speed at which the storm is developing.
   - The description and development of the storm is drawn out. The text begins by saying the storm "came slowly" and is then split into paragraphs which describe different aspects of the storm in detail. This emphasises to the reader how the storm took a long time to develop.
   - The focus of the extract starts in the streets of the city, even focusing in briefly on the "centre", before moving up to "the clouds" and up even further to be "high above" the clouds. After this, the focus returns to ground level, where "The gas lamps were lit". Shifting the focus gives the reader a complete picture of the events and allows them to track the storm's movements from several perspectives.

5. a) You should have talked about how the extract's structure creates tension. Here are some things you could have mentioned:
   - Describing the progress of the storm slowly builds up a sense of anticipation. Developments at each time-marker suggest the storm is building up to something and creates tension as the reader wonders what will happen next.
   - Shifting the perspective from the streets, to the clouds, to above the clouds shows the scale of the storm. This creates tension by highlighting how large the storm is and the amount of destruction it could cause.
   - In the first paragraph, different types of people in London are listed, such as "the tram drivers, the muffin-men, the cobblers and solicitors". This creates tension by highlighting all the people who will be affected by the storm.

   b) You should have talked about how the author's descriptions of people create tension in the extract, using examples to support your points. Here are some things you could have mentioned:
   - The author creates tension by showing how oblivious most people in London are to the coming "catastrophe". This lack of awareness is emphasised by the phrase "the city went on as normal". Tension is created through dramatic irony, as the reader knows something bad is coming.
   - "Palm-readers and fortune-tellers" are described as being "huddled fearfully" while "babies cried". These reactions suggest that some humans and animals know something is wrong, reinforcing the idea that something bad is going to happen which creates tension.

6. You should have given your opinion on the statement and explained your ideas using evidence from the text.
   If you agreed with the statement, you might have mentioned:
   - From the first paragraph, the storm is made to seem evil. The city is described as being "unaware of the horror bearing down upon it". The phrase "bearing down" suggests that the storm is moving aggressively towards the city, and this sense of threat is emphasised by the use of the phrase "the horror" to refer to the storm.
   - The phrase "a huge, rotating monstrosity of cloud" creates the impression of a giant predatory beast. The phrase "rotating monstrosity" suggests that the cloud is like a powerful monster circling the city. This makes the city seem threatened and leaves the reader with a sense of unease.
   - Darkness is used to create a sense of threat, because darkness often symbolises evil. The storm's darkness is so strong that the "gas lamps were lit at four o'clock". The gas lamps being lit so early shows that the storm's darkness is supernatural and emphasises to the reader that there is something unusual about the storm.

It's fine to disagree or partly agree with the statement — just make sure that you've used evidence from the text to back up your answer.

Section Four — Childhood

Pages 36-39: Exercise A — 'The Tiger's Wife'

1. a) Any four things about the grandfather, either directly quoted or paraphrased, from the first paragraph. Answers might include:
   - He is bald.
   - He wears a hat/raincoat.
   - He carries a copy of *The Jungle Book* in his pocket.
   - He is a doctor.

   b) You might have said that the grandfather seems caring. He brings food for the animals, such as "sugar cubes" for the pony, and he picks up his grandchild so she can "see the tigers". These examples show him caring for other creatures and people. You could have said that he is imaginative and charismatic. The grandfather offers the narrator a "fairy tale" which she can "imagine" herself in. This shows his ability to tell a gripping and fascinating story.

2. You should have given your opinion on the statement and explained your ideas using evidence from the text.
   If you agreed with the statement, you could have mentioned:
   - A close bond is established by the description of the journey to the zoo. The narrator describes "the certainty" of the journey they take, implying that it's a regular trip that she finds reassuring. This shows the grandfather and his grandchild spending frequent, quality time together.

   If you disagreed with the statement, you could have mentioned:
   - There is ambiguity about the state of the relationship. The granddaughter isn't "allowed to hold" the book, which implies the grandfather is strict. However, the grandfather "recites the passages" from the book to his granddaughter "all afternoon", which implies they have a caring relationship. These create contrasting impressions of their relationship.

Don't worry if you've taken a different viewpoint to this — just make sure you've used evidence from the text to support your view.

3. You should have talked about why you think the writer included the sentence and the effect it has on the reader. Here are some things you could have mentioned:
   - The reference to royalty suggests the writer is trying to make the castle's history sound exciting. This makes the reader want to know more about the history of the zoo.
   - The exciting image from the past contrasts with the "blocked-off troughs" and "rusted orange" bars of the present day. This contrast creates a sense of faded grandeur, emphasising how the castle isn't as luxurious as it once was.

4. You should have talked about how the structure helps to describe the narrator's memories and the effect this has on the reader. Here are some things you could have mentioned:
   - The first paragraph immediately states that this is the narrator's "earliest memory". By having this information in the first sentence, the writer makes the reader aware that they're going to read about a significant memory.
   - The memory is told chronologically. The writer may have done this so the reader could follow the narrator's journey through the zoo and share her experiences. This structure makes the memory easier for the reader to imagine.
   - The writer mentions tigers frequently throughout the extract, often in the first sentence of new paragraphs. This emphasises that the tigers are a significant feature of the narrator's memories, highlighting their importance to her.
   - At the end of the extract, the narrator says how "the smell" of the tigers will return at random points throughout her life. This shift to looking to the future emphasises the power of the memory to the reader.

Answers

5. You could have said that the present tense allows the reader to experience the memory just as the narrator did. You might have said this means the reader is absorbed in the action as it is happening, or you could have said it makes it easier for the reader to relate to the narrator's feelings.
6. You should have found an example from the text that suggests that this is a magical realist novel, e.g. because it hints at superstition, fantasy or myth, and explained your answer. Here are some things you could have mentioned:
   - The grandfather says "I once knew a girl who loved tigers so much she almost became one herself." This memory contains an element of fantasy and hints that magical realism may come into play later on in the novel.
   - The grandfather carries a copy of "The Jungle Book", a story with elements of fantasy, such as talking animals. The writer's choice to use this book hints that there may be fantasy elements (a feature of magical realism) in 'The Tiger's Wife'.
7. You should have given your opinion on the statement and explained your ideas using evidence from the text.
   If you agreed with the statement, you could have mentioned:
   - The writer uses sensory language to make the animals feel realistic. The writer describes the bears as "smelling of damp earth and the death of something". The reader can imagine this smell clearly, which makes it more likely that they will engage with the description of the bears and makes the memory feel more vivid.
   - The writer mentions numerous colours to paint a vivid picture of the setting, such as the "rusted orange" cage bars, the "blue bag" of food and the "gold-leaf" book cover. These images give visual detail to the memory, showing how clearly the narrator recalls events. The "gold-leaf" cover also indicates that the book is like a treasure and highlights the value the narrator puts on the time she spends with her grandfather when he reads to her.
   - The writer uses sensory language to create a clear image of the grandfather. For example, he is described as being as "bald as a stone" in the opening sentence. This creates a distinct visual image of the grandfather as having a smooth and shiny head. This simile could also give an insight into the grandfather's personality. The reference to "stone" suggests that the narrator sees her grandfather as a strong individual.

   If you disagreed with the statement, you could have said that:
   - It isn't sensory language that brings the setting to life, but a different technique. For example, you could have talked about the use of lists in the text. The writer describes the zoo by listing what's there: "the popcorn cart, the umbrella stand, a small kiosk". This populates the reader's idea of a zoo with specific details, bringing the memory to life.

Pages 40-43: Exercise B — 'The Little Stranger'

1. a) You should have summarised everything the reader is told about the Ayres family in the first paragraph. Here are some things you should have mentioned:
   - They were rich, but it is implied that they aren't anymore.
   - The family were popular/well-known in the district.
   - Mrs Ayres, the Colonel and Susan make up the Ayres family.
   - Mrs Ayres was twenty-four or twenty-five, the Colonel was slightly older, and their daughter, Susan, was about six.

   b) You should have written about your impression of the Ayres family in the extract as a whole and what gave you that impression. Here are some things you could have mentioned:
   - They care about protecting their house and social status. The narrator mentions the "rope or ribbon" tied across the doors and windows which blocked people from the village from entering. This shows the Ayres family as wanting to protect Hundreds Hall and implies that they did not want the everyday people of the village to be allowed in.
   - They are important in the community. This is implied by them hosting an event and "handing out commemorative medals", as well as the narrator saying that they were "big people in the district" at the time.

   Don't worry if you had a different impression — just make sure that you've used evidence from the extract to support your view.
2. You should have written why you think the writer set the extract on Empire Day and how it relates to the Ayres family. Here are some things you could have mentioned:
   - As Empire Day is no longer widely celebrated in the UK, it shows that the extract is set in the past. This places the memory, and the Ayres family, a long time ago.
   - Empire Day celebrated the British Empire's power. This could symbolically suggest that the Ayres family is powerful.
   - Empire Day slowly became less popular as the British Empire grew weaker. This could foreshadow the fate of the Ayres family — the use of "then" and "still" in the first paragraph suggests they also became less powerful.
3. a) You should have explained why the narrator tried to take the acorn. Here are the things you could have mentioned:
   - The narrator's admiration for Hundreds Hall meant he wanted to own a piece of it himself.
   - The narrator felt he was entitled to the acorn because he admired Hundreds Hall in a way other children didn't.

   You might even have mentioned that the narrator says the decorative border was unlike anything he had seen and implies that this was a reason he wanted to take the acorn. You shouldn't have mentioned vandalism, spite or destruction — the narrator says he <u>didn't</u> do it for these reasons.

   b) You should have said how the reader sees the narrator's character after he tries to take the acorn. Here are some things you could have mentioned:
   - The reader may see the narrator as a selfish character. Verbs such as "dug" show the force he used and imply the narrator is willing to damage property to get what he wants.
   - The reader may see the narrator as a remorseful character. The reader is told that he now sees what he did as a "dreadful thing". This suggests he feels guilty about his actions.
4. You should have compared the language the writer uses to present the servant's quarters to the rest of Hundreds Hall. Here are some things you could have mentioned:
   - The servant's quarters are presented as busy with people while the rest of Hundreds Hall is filled with objects. An "extraordinary number of people" fill the servant's quarters, which makes the number sound unusual, emphasising how busy it is. The upstairs of Hundreds Hall is "filled" with "things": "chairs and cabinets, the bevel of a looking-glass, the scroll of a frame". The use of a list makes Hundreds Hall seem full of items. Together, these descriptions emphasise the difference in the lifestyles between the relaxed and materialistic upper class and the hard working lower class.
   - The servant's quarters are presented as unpleasant whereas Hundreds Hall is described as luxurious. The servant's quarters have "the feel of a castle dungeon" which builds the perception that the quarters are unpleasant. In contrast, the upstairs of Hundreds Hall has "marbled-floored passages". Marble flooring has connotations of grandeur, making Hundreds Hall sound luxurious. This could suggest the value the Ayres family places on the servants — they are provided with an unpleasant work space while the luxurious upstairs part of Hundreds Hall is unpopulated. This suggests that the Ayres family do not value their servants or do not view them as important.
   - The writer presents a divide between the servant's quarters and the rest of Hundreds Hall through the "green baize curtain". The "baize" material is coarse and rough, indicating it is not nice to touch. This could suggest this boundary is unpleasant to cross, highlighting the differences between the servants quarters and the rest of Hundreds Hall.

Answers

5. You should have explained how you can tell the narrator is describing something that happened a long time ago. Here are some things you could have mentioned:
   - The narrator says that the Ayres family "still had most of their money then". This implies that they are no longer rich and that a change over a long period of time has occurred.
   - The narrator says the Ayres family must have been a "handsome family". This implies that the family doesn't look the same anymore, suggesting a long period of time has passed.
   - In the last paragraph, the narrator says "I was an obedient child". This suggests that the narrator is no longer a child, which indicates that a lot of time has gone by.
6. You should have given your opinion on the statement and explained your ideas using evidence from the text.
   If you agreed with the statement, you could have mentioned:
   - The narrator describes Hundreds Hall with fond detail. He remembers the hall's "lovely ageing details" and proceeds to list them. The use of the adjective "lovely" shows that he likes its old look, and the list of three, "the worn red brick, the cockled window glass, the weathered sandstone edgings", shows the details of the house are firmly cemented in his memory. His ability to acknowledge these details at such a young age, and his ability to remember these flaws implies his enduring interest in the house.
   - The structure shows the narrator's interest in the house. The text begins with his first memory of Hundreds Hall, and then each paragraph after describes different parts of the house in detail. Giving details about a variety of areas in the house shows the narrator's interest in Hundreds Hall.

   If you disagreed with the statement, you could have said:
   - The language used by the narrator implies that he is disinterested in the Ayres family, who live at Hundreds Hall. His "memory of them is vague", which suggests an indifference to the Ayres family — his "vague" memories suggest that they weren't important enough for him to remember. This contrasts with his strong memory of Hundreds Hall, which he recalls "most vividly". This shows the narrator's interest was in the hall itself, but not the people who lived there.

It's fine to partly agree with the statement — just make sure that you've used evidence from the text to back up your answer.

Pages 44-47: Exercise C — 'The Fishermen'

1. You should have given your impression of the father and referred to the writer's use of language to back up your ideas. Here are some things you could have mentioned:
   - The father is an intimidating person. The metaphor about his voice "tacked nine inches deep into the beams" of the children's minds creates an uncomfortable image for the reader and reflects how the father creates fear in his sons.
   - The father is implied to be distant from his children, such as when he "dropped" the "twenty-naira notes" for his sons. The use of "dropped" suggests carelessness, implying he isn't close to his children. The action could also suggest that the father is trying to replace his parental presence with money.
   - The father doesn't seem to respect his wife. This is shown when he starts the car while his wife is "still speaking" — the father was so impatient to leave that he didn't wait for his wife to finish. This shows a lack of respect for her.
2. a) You could have said that the narrator's mother is presented as being concerned about the family. She says "remember you have growing boys back here" to the father. This suggests that she feels as if the father is leaving them behind and hints at a concern that the family might fall apart.
   b) You could have said that the mother is presented as a provider for the family. She runs "a fresh food store in the open market" while looking after the narrator and his "five siblings". This shows the mother does a lot to look after her family.
   c) You should have given your opinion on the statement and explained your ideas using evidence from the text.
   If you agreed with the statement, you could have mentioned:
   - The narrator's mother isn't as important as the father in this extract, which is shown through the text's structure. The first four paragraphs are dedicated to the father, whereas the mother only gets a few mentions in the whole extract. This shows her lack of importance to this part of the story.

   If you disagreed with the statement, you could have mentioned:
   - The narrator's mother is important because she contrasts the father and emphasises his absence. The father goes "to work" while the mother "tended" to the children. This implies the father never looked after the children.
3. a) You should have written a summary of how the narrator felt about the past before and after his father left. Here are the things you could have mentioned:
   - Before his father moved, the narrator didn't care about the past — he says "We gave little thought to past events."
   - After his father left, the past became more important to the narrator — he began to "yearn and crave for it".

   b) You should have explained how language is used to describe the narrator's attitude to the future before his father left. Here are some things you could have mentioned:
   - The writer uses a simile to compare thoughts of the future to a train that is "treading tracks of hope". The use of a train could indicate the narrator being on course, and the tracks of "hope" indicate his optimism about the future. The alliteration in "train treading tracks" creates a regular rhythm that reflects the steady movement of a train. This emphasises the narrator's thoughts that his future was heading smoothly in a good direction.
   - The writer uses a list to show what the narrator felt he could achieve before his father left. He lists successful people: *"a pilot, or the president of Nigeria, rich man"*. Listing these people shows that he felt there were many successful paths to take and that he could achieve great things in the future.
   - The writer uses a metaphor to describe the future as a "blank canvas". Anything can be painted on a blank canvas, so this image reflects the narrator's belief that the future was full of possibilities.
4. You should have written about how the structure of the extract reflects the impact the events had on the narrator. Here are some things you could have mentioned:
   - After the father drives away, the narrator states "He was gone." This short, monosyllabic sentence is at the end of a paragraph, disrupting the flow of the narrative and emphasising how the father's departure unsettled the narrator's life and left him flat and subdued.
   - The last paragraph, where the narrator talks about the impact of his father's departure, is the longest in the extract and is nearly the length of the other paragraphs combined. The structure of this paragraph emphasises the impact of the father's departure. The narrator talks about life before the letter came and how "everything was in place". The use of "But" towards the end indicates a great change in his life — the moment when "equation of things" became unbalanced. Having this tonal shift towards the end, after the narrator has explained how life used to be good, makes the impact of the father's departure on the narrator's life seem greater. The writer's choice to focus heavily on the impact of the event in this way shows how much it affected the narrator's life.
5. You should have said how the narrator's life and experiences are presented, using evidence from the text to explain your answer. Here are some things you could have mentioned:
   - The writer uses language to present the narrator's life as split into two parts — before and after his father left. The narrator uses figurative language to describe the time before his father left. For example, when he says the clouds "filled with cupfuls of dust in the dry seasons". This plays down the

Answers

harsh conditions by suggesting there is only a small amount of dust, and creates a romanticised perception of the past. However, the narrator's father leaving "changed the equation of things". The use of the mathematical word "equation" here suggests that the narrator started to think about the world in a more logical and less romantic light, emphasising how his life changed after his father left.

- The text is structured to show how powerless the narrator was to change the course of his life. The narrator's reaction to his father leaving isn't made clear until the fifth paragraph after his father had "left the room". This indicates the father's overpowering nature and the narrator's inability to try and "make sense" of things until after his father had left the room. This creates a sense of helplessness by making the narrator seem unable to understand his father's departure and what it might mean for himself and his family.
- The extract is mostly written in a serious tone, but the tone changes in the last paragraph when the narrator recalls the past before his father leaves. For example, the narrator uses onomatopoeia when describing the train as having a loud "elephantine toot". Onomatopoeic sounds such as "toot" are often used by children, which make them seem playful, and the use of "elephantine" creates humour by associating the train with an animal. This indicates that the narrator is more relaxed thinking about the time before his father left.

Section Five — Appearances

Pages 48-51: Exercise A — 'Larry's Party'

1. a) You should given three examples where a simile or metaphor has been used to describe the jackets and explained the effect each one has on the reader. Here are some things you could have mentioned:
   - Describing the pocket of the new jacket as "a silky void" makes it seem like it is incredibly comfortable. The adjective "silky" implies that the material is soft and smooth and the noun "void" suggests that the pocket seems to be endless. This gives the reader an impression of great and lasting comfort.
   - Describing the lint as "like meteor grit" makes the pockets of Larry's old jacket seem rough. The "grit" creates the impression that the lint is coarse. The adjective "meteor" creates the image of the lint as small rocks floating in space. This makes the pockets seem like a place with no atmosphere and emphasises their discomfort.
   - Describing the pattern on the buttons of the new jacket as "like a pecan pie cut into quarters" implies that the buttons are as satisfying to look at as food is to eat. Their inviting appearance is emphasised by the repeated, plosive 'p' sound in "pecan pie" which imitates the sound of lips smacking hungrily.

   b) You should have talked about other ways language is used to describe the jackets to the reader, using examples to support your points. Here are some things you could have mentioned:
   - Personification is used to describe how the "waves" on the buttons of the more valuable jacket met in the middle and "dived down there in a dark center and disappeared." Associating the buttons with a brave human activity like diving emphasises their bold style and implies that they add character to the jacket.
   - Sensory language is used to describe the more valuable jacket. The phrase "You could feel the raised design with your finger" encourages the reader to imagine touching the jacket. This helps the reader to feel involved in the story and makes it seem more realistic.

2. You should have given your opinion on the statement and explained your ideas using evidence from the text.
   If you agreed with the statement, you might have mentioned:
   - The descriptions of Larry's surroundings are very vague. The writer only uses generic phrases, such as "the coffee shop" and "the bus stop", which makes it difficult for the reader to fully picture the scene in this extract.
   - The focus on the jacket means that the reader doesn't learn very much about Larry's own appearance. This makes it difficult to imagine Larry wearing the jacket.

   If you disagreed with the statement, you might have mentioned:
   - Focusing on the jacket is a good way of showing the reader how important outward appearances are to Larry. When he starts wearing a jacket "twice the value of his own", he stops paying attention to the world around him and focuses on his "hot new" jacket. The vague descriptions of Larry's surroundings reflect his changed focus, emphasising the jacket's significance to him because of how he looks in it.
   - Using most of the extract to describe the jacket Larry picks up is an effective way of emphasising the large effect it has on him. The lack of descriptions about the rest of his appearance means that the jacket is the only thing about Larry that the reader can picture in their head which suggests that the jacket has given Larry a new identity.

You could have talked about how avoiding descriptions of Larry's surroundings might emphasise how boring Larry considers his everyday life.

3. You should have talked about how the extract is structured to interest the reader. Here are some things you could have said:
   - The text is structured to make the reader interested in Larry and his jacket. Lines 3-14 give in-depth descriptions of the jacket which help the reader to picture it clearly in their minds. The focus then moves to Larry's thoughts about the jacket. This intrigues the reader as they wonder what he will do with it and also gives an interesting insight into his character. The focus then returns to the jacket in lines 25-38 with more detailed descriptions of it. This shows Larry's infatuation with it, which is amusing to the reader.
   - The structure of the extract engages the reader with Larry's thoughts. The extract is made up of several short paragraphs which imitate the many different thoughts that pop into Larry's head as he walks. The sudden and frequent changes of topic make the reader feel like they are experiencing the thoughts at the same time as Larry, which involves them in the extract.

4. You should have talked about how the language of the extract helps the reader understand Larry's thoughts and personality. Here are some things you could have mentioned:
   - Onomatopoeic language emphasises how much more confident Larry feels wearing the new jacket. The word "bam" describes how he brings his shoulders forward powerfully as he walks. This emphasises how assertive Larry feels and could imply that he is usually less self-assured.
   - The capitalisation of "Big Guy" suggests that Larry feels more important in the more valuable jacket. Capitalising these words makes it seem as though he is giving himself a title, which suggests he feels he is a person of significance.
   - Larry describes the jacket very specifically at the end of the extract, mentioning its "mixed shades of brown", "freckled tobacco tones" and "subtle orange flecks". This suggests that Larry is very observant and has a keen eye for detail.
   - Larry uses lots of technical language, describing the jacket with words and phrases such as "warp and woof", "quadrants" and "intersected". These terms give the impression that Larry is an intelligent man because they are not especially common.

Pages 52-55: Exercise B — 'The Picture of Dorian Gray'

1. Any four things about the bedroom, either directly quoted or paraphrased, from lines 1-6. Answers might include:
   - It is shaped like an octagon.
   - It is on the ground floor.
   - Dorian has recently decorated it.
   - There are tapestries on the wall.

Answers

2. You should have given at least two examples of how light is described in the first two paragraphs and explained their effect. Here are some things you could have mentioned:
   - Wilde refers to the light in the library as "arrested light" which "struggled" to get through the blinds. This suggests that the light is being refused entry and that darkness is a powerful oppressive force. As darkness is often seen as a symbol of evil, this creates an ominous mood for the reader.
   - The metaphor "The bright dawn flooded the room" emphasises the brightness of the sunlight by suggesting that it rushes into the room and overwhelms it. This light also appears to have a purifying force — it "swept" the menacing-sounding "fantastic shadows" into the corner of the room. Because light is often regarded as a symbol for good, this suggests the idea of good versus evil to the reader.
3. You should have talked about how Wilde conveys Dorian's thoughts and feelings about Sybil to the reader. Here are some things you could have mentioned:
   - The use of the one-word exclamation "Cruelty!" could suggest that Dorian scoffs at the idea that he had acted cruelly towards Sibyl.
   - Rhetorical questions emphasise how Dorian believes that he hasn't done anything wrong — he asks himself "Had he been cruel?", before claiming that it was "the girl's fault" and that he is blameless.
4. You should have talked about what you think the overall tone of the extract is using evidence from the text. Here are some things you could have mentioned:
   - The extract has a confused tone. Dorian goes from believing that the change in the painting is "apparent" to later claiming that the picture "had not changed". These contradictory statements highlight the turmoil he is experiencing which add to the confused tone of the extract.
   - The extract has a panicked tone as a result of Dorian's growing alarm over the painting. Negative words such as "horribly" and "monstrous" reinforce Dorian's distress, and the run-on sentences in lines 22-25 reflect his worries over the wish he made. These devices make his anxieties clear, which contribute to the panicked tone.
5. You should have given your opinion on the statement and explained your ideas using evidence from the text.
   If you agreed with the statement, you could have mentioned:
   - The painting is mentioned in almost every paragraph, which focuses the reader's attention on it. This structure reflects how Dorian keeps thinking about the painting, which shows that it is an important part of the extract.
   - The writer keeps returning the reader's focus to the painting by having Dorian repeatedly looking at the painting, moving away from it and then looking at it "again". Frequently returning the focus of the text to the painting in this way implies that Dorian is very concerned by it, which makes it an important focus of this extract.

   If you disagreed with the statement, you could have mentioned:
   - The extract is focused on Dorian himself rather than the painting. The reader isn't told much detail about the portrait, only that there is a "touch of cruelty in the mouth." On the other hand, there are detailed references to Dorian's thoughts and behaviour throughout the extract.

It is possible to partly agree with the statement. For example, you may have said that the extract is focused on the painting throughout, but only to highlight Dorian's emotional reaction to it.

6. You should have talked about how the writer shows Dorian's attitude towards the painting and explained your answer using evidence from the text. Here are some things you could have mentioned:
   - Dorian's attitude changes from acknowledging what he sees in the painting ("The expression looked different") at the start of the extract, to denying what he saw ("The picture had not changed"). This complete change in opinion emphasises Dorian's conflicted attitudes towards the painting and highlights how much it troubles him.
   - The extract is structured to show how Dorian's attitude towards the painting is conflicted. In the final four paragraphs, he alternates between pondering the possibility that the painting is bearing "the burden" of his sins and asserting that it is "folly" to think the picture has changed. Starting a new paragraph every time his attitude changes emphasises the difference between these attitudes and that he's struggling to make sense of the painting.
   - Dorian's attitude to the painting is one of concern. This is reflected in the use of several questions in the second-to-last paragraph, such as "But the picture? What was he to say of that?". This self-questioning suggests doubt and uncertainty which emphasises Dorian's worried attitude towards the painting.

Pages 56-59: Exercise C — 'Norwegian Wood'

1. Any four things that Watanabe sees while walking in the meadow, either directly quoted or paraphrased, from lines 1-8. Answers might include:
   - The mountains
   - Grasses that are "head-high"
   - A nearby wood
   - Two "bright red" birds
2. You should have talked about how the writer creates the impression that the narrator vividly remembers the meadow scene. Here are some things you could have said:
   - The meadow scene happened 18 years ago, but the narrator can "still" remember "every detail". 18 years is a long time to have passed, so the fact that he can still remember the scene in such detail shows what a vivid memory it is.
   - The narrator gives specific details about what he saw. For example, he describes the vivid colours of nature like the "deep, brilliant green" mountains and the "frozen blue" sky. The adjectives "deep", "brilliant" and "frozen" to describe the colours are details which show how well the narrator can picture the scene in his mind.
   - The narrator mentions the sounds of "distant barking" and the "rustle" of branches. These are surprising things for someone to remember 18 years later because they are both fairly quiet and insignificant sounds, which emphasises how vivid the narrator's memory of the scene is.
3. You should have talked about how the writer uses language to show what the narrator was like as a young man in the second paragraph and explained the effect of this. Here are some things you could have mentioned:
   - The narrator is presented as being in love as a young man. The use of strong language to describe how he "didn't give a damn" about the scenery emphasises how his focus was purely on Naoko, which shows how infatuated he was with her. The use of the adjective "beautiful" to describe her further highlights the attraction he felt towards her.
   - The narrator seemed to be more self-centred as a young man. He says that he thought "about myself" and then "about myself again" — this repetition, emphasised by the simile of how his thoughts "came back, like a boomerang" to him, reinforces how his mind always returned to himself.
   - The narrator is presented as having had a troubled love affair as a young man. The repetition of "love" emphasises the love he felt for Naoko, but also highlights that this love was problematic — the second reference to love is to say that it came with "complications".
4. You should have talked about how the writer has used structure to keep the reader interested. Here are some things you could have mentioned:
   - The first paragraph focuses on the landscape, which effectively sets the scene for the reader. Vivid descriptions, such as the mountains "Washed clean of summer's dust",

Answers

and the "streak of cloud hung pasted across a dome of frozen blue", help the reader to picture the scene well, and engages them in the story through such clear and interesting descriptions.
- Changes of focus in the extract keep the reader interested. The first paragraph focuses mainly on scenery and gives little detail of characters, while the second focuses more on the narrator's thoughts and feelings towards Naoko to feed the reader some information about the characters. However, the third paragraph returns to focus on the scenery, which teases the reader because they are likely to want to know more about the characters. The fourth paragraph finally returns to describe Naoko in detail.
- The extract keeps the reader interested by slowly giving information about Naoko. She is only briefly referred to in the first three paragraphs with the narrator mentioning "her hair" and that she is "beautiful". This makes the reader want to read on to find out more about her. It's only in the final paragraph that more detail is finally given about Naoko, such as her "tiny, cold hand" and "straight, black hair".

5. You should have talked about why you think the writer chooses to describe Naoko in the way that he does. Here are some things you could have mentioned:
   - The writer gives small, specific details about Naoko in the final paragraph, which mimics the way in which Watanabe starts "joining images" of her in his memory. This gives the reader an incomplete image of Naoko to reflect how Watanabe struggles to picture her in his head. This creates mystery, as the reader wants to know more about her.
   - Naoko is described "in profile", describing her from the side, which is how Watanabe saw her when they used to walk together. This puts the reader in Watanabe's shoes so that they can imagine they are "side by side" with Naoko, but it means that they are unable to fully imagine her face. This makes the reader curious about her and also reflects Watanabe's hazy memory.
   - The descriptions of Naoko as "cold" might reflect Watanabe's feelings towards her now. Her "tiny, cold hand" and hair which was "cool to the touch" could both represent the physical and emotional distance he feels towards her now that he is older.
6. You should have given your opinion on the statement and explained your ideas using evidence from the text.
   If you agreed with the statement, you could have mentioned:
   - Watanabe's love for Naoko is evident in his descriptions of her. The last sentence of the extract details the way Naoko looks into Wantanabe's eyes, using a simile to say she looked as if trying to spot a "minnow that has darted across the pool of a limpid spring". This simile creates a tranquil image of nature, with the adjective "limpid" creating a sense of a pure and perfect moment. This creates an affectionate tone, reflecting the narrator's continued love.
   - Watanabe seems to appreciate all aspects of Naoko's appearance, which reflects his ongoing love for her. His appreciation is suggested in the way he tenderly describes her "soft, rounded earlobe" and "microscopic mole". Remembering these small details, which are not usual signs of beauty, implies that he still has deep feelings for her.
   - Watanabe clearly wishes he could still be with Naoko. He thinks about his fading memories of her and asks "where could they have all gone?" This shows how important these memories are to him and suggests that he wants those times back. The use of three questions in lines 19-22 conveys Watanabe's sense of confusion over losing his memories of Naoko and implies that he feels despair that "such a thing" has happened.

   If you disagreed with the statement, you could have mentioned:
   - Watanabe says that he "was in love" 18 years ago. The use of the past tense in this phrase suggests that he is no longer in love with Naoko and has moved on with his life.
   - Watanabe says that "No one" is in the meadow scene that he is remembering. Because he is unable to picture either himself or Naoko in the meadow, the reader gets the impression that she isn't relevant to his life anymore. However, he spends "time" trying to remember her face, suggesting that the memory of her is still important to him.
   - The fact that Watanabe struggles to remember Naoko's face suggests that he isn't still in love with her. Having to "start joining images" of her together suggests to the reader that this may be the first time he's thought of her in a long time, and if he was still in love with her, he would have thought about her much more.

It is possible to partly agree with the statement. For example, you may have said that Watanabe still loves Naoko, but that he isn't in despair — he accepts that she is no longer a part of his life.

Section Six — Memories of the Past

Pages 60-63: Exercise A — 'The Shadow of the Wind'

1. You should have explained how the writer tries to draw the reader's interest in the first sentence of the extract. Here are some things you could have mentioned:
   - The writer mentions the Cemetery of Forgotten Books but doesn't explain what it is and why it is important, which makes the reader want to find out more.
   - The narrator says that he still remembers the day his father took him to the Cemetery of Forgotten Books, which hints that it was a significant event.
2. a) Any two examples of light and / or dark language from the text. Answers might include:
   - "dawn poured over Rambla de Santa Mónica"
   - "the sad smile that followed him like a shadow"
   - "talking to my mother in the darkness of my bedroom"
   - "I woke up screaming at first light."
   - "We looked at each other in the half-light"
   - "let in the pale glint of dawn."

   b) You should have explained the effect of each example you chose. Here are some things you could have mentioned:
   - The description of how the "dawn poured over Rambla de Santa Mónica" makes Barcelona sound beautiful and emphasises how the early morning light filled the street.
   - The father's grief over his wife's death is shown in the "sad smile that followed him like a shadow". This simile emphasises how his sorrow never leaves him.

Any explanations about the effect of light or dark language are okay — just make sure that you've linked your opinions back to the examples from the text.

3. You should have explained how language has been used to present books in a mysterious and exciting way. Here are some things you could have mentioned:
   - The narrator describes his grandfather's book shop as "an enchanted bazaar", which makes books sound magical.
   - The narrator says that he made "invisible friends" from the books he read, which makes it seem as though the characters he read about came to life.
   - The narrator says that, "to this day", his hands carry the smell of the books in his grandfather's shop. This could imply that they have a lasting power over him.
4. You should have talked about the effect of the non-linear structure. Here are some things you could have mentioned:
   - The non-linear structure creates suspense by introducing the Cemetery of Forgotten Books at the start and then making the reader wait to find out what it is. Delaying the explanation of the Cemetery (a place linked to death) creates a sense of mystery and an ominous mood.
   - The structure puts the father's behaviour in context. For example, the narrator's father gives a "sad smile" when the narrator mentions his mother. The narrator then goes on to explain that his mother died, which allows the reader to understand the father's earlier emotions.

Answers

5. You should have said why you think the writer has chosen to use an adult narrator and whether you think the text would be different if the narrator was still a child. Here are some things you could have mentioned:
   - The writer chooses to use an adult narrator to give the reader extra information that a child narrator would not have been able to give. For example, the narrator tells us that the "sad smile" the father gave in line 7 followed him "all through his life".
   - An adult narrator is able to analyse past feelings, behaviour and events. For example, the narrator says that when he was 10, his mother's absence was like a "deafening silence" that he "had not yet learned to stifle with words." The narrator's understanding of how he coped with his mother's absence is quite sophisticated — a child narrator might not have been able to express or understand these ideas.
   - The writer uses an adult narrator looking back on events to create interest. The extract begins "I still remember the day", indicating that the events to follow are important. This interests the reader in a way that's less achievable than if the narrator was still a child and describing events as they happened. This is because he wouldn't be able to judge how important those events might be.
6. You should have given an opinion on whether you think the extract shows how important family love can be and used evidence from the text to back up your answer. Here are some things you could have mentioned:
   - The bond between Daniel and his father is strong, which provides support for Daniel after his mother's death. When Daniel can't remember his mother's face, his father says, "I'll remember for both of us". This shows the father comforting Daniel, and the first-person plural "us" suggests that the father sees himself and Daniel as a partnership.
   - The extract shows how much Daniel still misses his mother. He describes falling asleep talking to her and being able to feel her "radiance and her warmth" in the house. The fact that he still speaks to her and feels her presence after she has died shows how important her presence was to him.

It's okay if you disagree with the statement — just make sure you can support your opinion with evidence from the text.

7. You should have written about how the writer uses language to create a sense of grief and loss in this extract. Here are some things you could have mentioned:
   - The writer uses an oxymoron to describe the absence of Daniel's mother as a "deafening silence". The contrasting words create a jarring effect, emphasising how unsettled and upset the loss makes Daniel and his father feel.
   - Daniel says that his mother's "radiance and her warmth haunted" their home. The comfort suggested by "radiance" and "warmth" contrasts with the use of the word "haunted", which usually has negative connotations. This suggests that while memories of his mother offer comfort to Daniel, he still feels her loss very deeply.
   - Daniel feels as though his "very soul was trying to escape" when he wakes up and realises he can't remember his mother's face. The "soul" is regarded as being the essence of a human being, so by using a simile to say it was trying to escape implies that Daniel feels as though he is being ripped apart by losing memories of his mother. This emphasises the grief he feels over her death.

Pages 64-67: Exercise B — 'The Kite Runner'

1. Any four things about Amir, either directly quoted or paraphrased, from the correct part of the extract.
   Answers might include:
   - He has a friend called Rahim Khan.
   - He has "unatoned sins" in his past.
   - He now lives in San Francisco.
   - He knows someone called Hassan.
2. You could have said that the two kites represent Amir and Hassan. Amir hears Hassan's voice in his head after he sees the kites, which suggests they are linked to Hassan. The two boys used to fly kites together in Afghanistan, which is why the author has chosen to use kites to represent them. Or, you could have mentioned that the kites seem to remind the narrator of Hassan, which gives him an opportunity in the narrative to begin telling their story.
3. You should have explained how Hosseini uses structure to set up the story in this extract. Here are some things you could have mentioned:
   - The narrator makes Hassan the focus of the extract and draws attention to his importance from the very first paragraph by ending it with the phrase "Hassan the harelipped kite runner". Ending the opening paragraph by giving Hassan a title indicates his significance to the rest of the story.
   - In the second paragraph, the narrator mentions names from his past: "I thought about Hassan. Thought about Baba. Ali." Presenting these names early in the extract suggests they will be important to the story.
4. a) You should have explained why you think Hassan is described as being like a "doll". Here are some things you could have mentioned:
   - It suggests that Hassan is treated like a belonging.
   - It suggests that Hassan is fragile or vulnerable.
   - It suggests that Amir can make Hassan do what he wants.

   b) You should have talked about other ways Hosseini uses language to describe Hassan and explained the effect they have on the reader's impression of him. Here are some things you could have mentioned:
   - Hosseini describes Hassan's eyes as "gold, green, even sapphire." Comparing his eyes to precious metal and jewels makes them sound beautiful and hints that Amir's memories of Hassan are somewhat idealised.
   - The description of Hassan's face as "almost perfectly round" makes him seem like a baby, perhaps suggesting that he is innocent or vulnerable.
5. You should have explained how Hosseini presents the relationship between Amir and Hassan, using evidence from the extract. Here are some things you could have mentioned:
   - Hosseini presents the relationship as being typical of a friendship between two young boys. Amir describes how they used to "climb the poplar trees" and mischievously "annoy" their neighbours. Giving a detailed account of their playful, childish past shows how strong Amir's memory is, indicating their friendship was also strong.
   - Their friendship is presented as a happy one — Amir and Hassan playfully throw mulberries at each other while "giggling" and "laughing". Using two verbs to describe their laughter emphasises the happiness in their friendship.
   - Hosseini presents the relationship as being imbalanced, with Amir being more dominant. Amir says that if he "asked, *really* asked" then Hassan would fire his slingshot at the neighbour's dog despite not wanting to. The repetition of "asked" shows how Amir was able to manipulate Hassan by asking him again and again.
   - The relationship is presented as being potentially unhealthy because Hassan seems overly submissive and loyal to Amir. He is described as "never" denying Amir anything and "never" tells his father that firing walnuts at the neighbour's dog was Amir's idea. The repetition of the strong adverb "never" emphasises Hassan's loyalty to Amir because it shows that he didn't waver in his faithfulness to him.
6. You should have given your opinion on the statement and explained your ideas using evidence from the text.
   If you agreed with the statement, you could have mentioned:
   - The writer gives detailed descriptions of Amir and Hassan playing together. He includes details such as the kind of tree they sat in, where in the tree they sat and how their "naked

Answers

feet" dangled from it. This level of detail helps the reader to picture the scene more clearly.
- The writer's descriptions of Amir's family home help the reader to imagine the kind of life that Amir lived as a child. It is obvious from the descriptions of the house that Amir's father is relatively rich. It is "sprawling", which emphasises its large size, and the "intricate" mosaic tiles on the bathroom floor indicate a fine level of detail and expense. All this helps to bring Amir's childhood to life for the reader.
- The writer describes people from Amir's past vividly. For example, the image of Ali wagging his finger at Amir and Hassan, and the way he compares them to the "devil" creates humour. This helps the reader get a sense of his personality and makes him seem like a more lifelike character.

You could have disagreed or only partially agreed with the statement — as long as you use evidence to back up your opinion.

Pages 68-71: Exercise C — 'The Garden of Evening Mists'

1. Any four things about the wall, either directly quoted or paraphrased, from the correct part of the extract.
   Answers might include:
   - The wall is high.
   - The wall has moss on it.
   - The wall has old water stains on it.
   - Ferns grow from the cracks in the wall.
   - There is a door in the wall.
2. You should have given three examples of language techniques the writer uses to describe the garden in lines 10-20 and explained their effect. For example:
   Technique: Metaphor
   Example: "the broken mosaic of sunlight"
   Effect: This metaphor encourages the reader to imagine small, tile-shaped areas of sunlight, which suggest that the sunlight is being filtered through leaves.
   Technique: Sensory language
   Example: "the scent of pine resin sticking to the air"
   Effect: This engages the reader's sense of smell and encourages them to imagine the scent themselves.
   Technique: Personification
   Example: "its branches sipping from the pond"
   Effect: This allows the reader to imagine how the branches are gently making contact with the surface of the water. This also makes the garden seem more alive.
3. You should have explained how the writer presents the narrator's relationship with Frederik Pretorius using evidence from the extract. Here are some things you could have said:
   - The relationship is portrayed as distant at first. Frederick stands "a few paces away" so he and the narrator can "study one another". The physical distance indicates that the pair aren't close, and their studying of each other in silence suggests that they don't feel immediately comfortable enough with each other to begin talking.
   - Frederik is presented as the one who made the effort to keep their friendship alive. The pair would only meet when Frederik "came down to Kuala Lumpur" because the narrator always "resisted" his invitations for her to visit him. This presents the narrator as unwilling and reluctant to visit Frederik and shows how one-sided their relationship is. However, the narrator does claim that Frederik "was the only close friend I would ever have", showing an appreciation of their friendship.
   - The pair are shown to have a kind of connection. Frederik tells the narrator that he feels she was "looking back to the past" when she was watching the bird. This suggests that he is able to tell what she's thinking, which shows a level of closeness and understanding between the two of them.
4. You should have written about how the structure of the extract makes it interesting for the reader. Here are some things you could have mentioned:
   - The writer begins by describing the wall that surrounds the garden, before describing the door and then the plaque which reads 'Evening Mists'. Gradually narrowing the focus in this way draws the reader's attention from the surroundings to the plaque. This highlights the importance of the plaque, which also adds to the suspense that's created when the words on the plaque are left unexplained. This makes the reader want to know what's behind the door.
   - In the second paragraph, the narrator pauses before entering the garden. This heightens the suspense by making the reader wait to find out what's inside. At the end of the paragraph, the narrator enters the garden and closes the door behind her. Having a paragraph break here creates a short pause, adding to the suspense and making the reader want to read on to find out what the garden is like.
   - The extract ends with the narrator saying that she "was thinking of the old days." Ending with this thought suggests that the past will play a large role in the rest of the story. It also creates intrigue in the reader as to what happened in the past between the narrator and Frederik, and how that might affect the events in the story. This leaves the reader with questions and they'll want to read on to find out the answers.
5. You should have given your opinion on the statement and explained your ideas using evidence from the text.
   If you agreed with the statement, you could have mentioned:
   - The narrator stares at the path through the mountains "for a few moments" as if she "might glimpse Aritomo walking home". This suggests that she is nostalgic because it seems that she really wants to see this character from her past, even if it's just briefly. The narrator is then described as "Shaking" her head, a verb which suggests she has to force herself to stop dwelling on the past. This makes the reader feel sympathy for her because it's as though she is admitting to herself that she's unlikely to see Aritomo again.
   - The narrator is clearly nostalgic because she wishes that the heron in the garden is the same one that was there when she first came to Yuguri, saying that she "wanted to believe" the bird had slipped "through the fingers of time". This metaphor presents time as oppressive, as though everyone experiences the passage of time in its grasp whether they like it or not. This creates sympathy for the narrator by implying she's sad that she is unable revisit the past.
   - At the end of the extract, the narrator says that she was thinking of "the old days", which hints at a sense of nostalgia for them. Shortly before she says this, the mist moving from the water's surface is described as "whispers only the wind could catch". This links the past with mist and whispers in the reader's mind, which emphasises how the past, like mist and whispers, is temporary and quick to fade. This highlights how she will never be able to experience the past she feels so nostalgic about again, which makes the reader feel sympathy for her.

   If you disagreed with the statement, you could have mentioned:
   - While the narrator remembers the garden from her past, she doesn't express a desire to go back in time. She says she has "always resisted" invitations to return, which implies that she has complicated feelings about the garden. Her refusal to return until now could also encourage the reader to think she is uncaring, because Frederik made the effort to visit her whenever he was in Kuala Lumpur.

It's fine to partly agree with the statement — just make sure that you've used evidence from the text to back up your answer.

Acknowledgements

We would like to thank the following copyright holders:

'MR NORRIS CHANGES TRAINS' by Christopher Isherwood. Copyright © 1935, Christopher Isherwood, used by permission of The Wylie Agency (UK) Limited.

'The Thirteenth Tale' by Diane Setterfield. The Orion Publishing Group, London. Copyright © Diane Setterfield 2006.

'The Miniaturist' by Jessie Burton. Copyright © Peebo & Pilgrim Limited 2014. Reproduced with permission of the Licensor through PLSclear.

'Life of Pi' by Yann Martel. Permission granted by Canongate Books Ltd. Copyright © Yann Martel, 2001.

'The Haunting of Hill House' by Shirley Jackson (Penguin Classics, 2013). Copyright © Shirley Jackson, 1959. Copyright renewed © Laurence Hyman, Barry Hyman, Sarah Webster and Joanne Shnurer, 1987. Reproduced by permission of Penguin Books Ltd.

'The Haunting of Alaizabel Cray'. Copyright © Chris Wooding, 2001, 2002, 2006, 2013. Reproduced with the permission of Scholastic Ltd. All rights reserved.

'The Tiger's Wife' by Téa Obreht. Published by The Orion Publishing Group, London. © Téa Obreht 2011.

'The Little Stranger' by Sarah Waters. Published by Little, Brown Book Group. © Sarah Waters 2009.

Extract from 'The Fishermen' by Chigozie Obioma, Published by ONE, an imprint of Pushkin Press, 2015.

Carol Shields: 'Larry's Party' (Fourth Estate, 2010). Copyright © 1997 Carol Shields. Reprinted by permission of the author.

Extract from 'Norwegian Wood' by Haruki Murakami. Copyright © 2000 by Haruki Murakami. Published by Vintage, a division of Random House LLC. Reproduced with permission from ICM Partners.

'The Shadow of the Wind' by Carlos Ruiz Zafón. The Orion Publishing Group, London. © Carlos Ruiz Zafón 2001.

© 2003 by Khaled Hosseini. 'The Kite Runner'. Bloomsbury Publishing Plc.

Extract from 'The Garden of Evening Mists' by Tan Twan Eng appears by permission of the publishers, Myrmidon Books Limited, Newcastle upon Tyne, England.

The extracts in this book have been carefully selected to develop GCSE students' English Language skills. CGP accepts no further responsibility for the content of published works by their authors.

ENCAWF41